Spring Harvest Praise

2008/09

SPRING HARVEST
Equipping the Church for action

Copyright and photocopying

No part of this publication may be reproduced in any form without the permission of the copyright holder of the songs and the publisher of the songbook. Exceptions to this rule are made for holders of licences issued by Christian Copyright Licensing International as follows:

Church Copyright Licence:

    churches and organisations holding this licence may reproduce the words of the songs within the terms of their licence.

Music Reproduction Licence:

    churches and organisations holding this licence may reproduce the music of the songs within the terms of their licence.

For information about the above licences, contact:

For UK and Europe –   Christian Copyright Licensing (Europe) Ltd,

           P.O. Box 1339, Eastbourne, East Sussex, BN21 1AD.

For USA and Canada –   Christian Copyright Licensing Inc,

           17201 NE Sacramento Street, Portland, Oregon 97230, USA

Australasia –   Christian Copyright Licensing Asia Pacific Pty Ltd, P.O. Box 664,

           Baulkham Hills Business Centre, Sydney, NSW 2153, Australia

Africa –   Christian Copyright Licensing Africa Pty Ltd, P.O. Box 2347,

           Durbanville 7551, South Africa

UNAUTHORISED PHOTOCOPYING IS ILLEGAL and detrimental to the work and ministry of the songwriters and publishers.

All rights reserved. All songs are reproduced by kind permission of the copyright holders – details of which are shown beneath each song/hymn. Any omission of acknowledgement to composer or publisher will be corrected in future editions.

Acknowledgements

Scripture quotations taken from the HOLY BIBLE, NEW INTERNATIONAL VERSION.
Copyright © 1973, 1978, 1984 by International Bible Society. Used by permission of Hodder and Stoughton Limited. All rights reserved. "NIV" is a registered trade mark of International Bible Society. UK trademark number 1448790

Music type setting and new arrangements by David Ball, davidoxon@aol.com
Cover design by Dan Armstrong
Printed in England by Halcyon

Published by Spring Harvest, 14 Horsted Square, Uckfield, East Sussex, TN22 1QG, UK.
Spring Harvest. A Registered Charity.
Distributed by ICC, Silverdale Road, Eastbourne, East Sussex, BN20 7AB, UK.

Spring Harvest wishes to acknowledge and thank the following people for their help in the compilation and production of this songbook:
Andrew Crookall, Andy Flannagan, Calvin Hollingworth, Cheryl Jenkinson, Phil Loose, David Peacock, Kate Silber, and Spring Harvest Head Office staff.
Thank you to John Bell, Marie Birkinshaw, Fiona Jo Clark, Jo Doré, Mark Earey, Andy Flanangan, Keith Getty, Mel Holden, John Leach, Martin Leckebusch, Randle Manwaring, Noel Robinson, Northumbria Community, Ruth Sermon, Kate Silber and Pat Turner for liturgy and worship tips.

ISBN 978-1-899788-61-3

Contents

Songs are listed in order of first line, not title. In a few cases, alphabetical ordering of songs has been changed slightly, in order to ensure that page turns are not needed in any two-page songs.

The words edition of this songbook is also available in Braille and Giant print

Index
Song titles differing from first lines are in italics

Online access to guitar chords, formatted song words, OHP masters and liturgy for Spring Harvest Praise 2008/09 songbook owners only

Please visit: www2.springharvest.org/guitarchords08/
User name: 08guitarchords
Password: pH9Y4qECawe7r

Please ensure that you have the relevant permissions before printing, photocopying, reproducing or displaying any items from the above password protected pdf's. Do not email the download or pass this link to people who haven't bought the songbook. Please also note that no third party use is permitted for commercial or display use.

If you wish to reproduce the guitar chords, OHP masters or liturgy in addition to your initial download:

1. **Please ensure your church holds the appropriate licence from Christian Copyright Licensing. If in doubt, or to purchase a licence, go to www.ccli.co.uk email: sales@ccli.co.uk or call 01323 436103**
2. **Make sure that whoever is responsible for your church's CCLI licence adds the relevant songs to the annual report as being reproduced from Spring Harvest Praise 2008/09.**

If you do not have the relevant licence from CCLI, or for any song or liturgies not covered by your CCLI licence, you will need to contact the individual copyright owner(s) AND Spring Harvest for permission to reproduce. A list of addresses can be found on the above web page or printed under the relevant song in the songbook.

1

A thousand times I've failed
(From the inside out)

Joel Houston

(continued over...)

This song is recorded on the Spring Harvest New Songs 'Wonderful Saviour' album

ing, your glo-ry goes be-yond all fame. And the cry____ of my heart____ is to bring____

_ you praise, from the in - side out. Lord, my soul____ cries out. E-ver-last-

_ cries out. From the in - side out. Lord, my soul____ cries out, Lord.____

1a   Walking but not listening
Based on John 14:9

Have I been walking, but not listening?
Grown familiar with the King of kings?
Forgotten who you are?
Have I not listened?
Not attempted to hear, not expected to hear your voice?
Spirit of truth, teach me, I want to know more.
I want to know Jesus

All around your throne

Sue Rinaldi

1. All a - round your throne there are an - gels sing - ing,
2. All a - round your throne there are prai - ses ris - ing,
3. All a - round your throne ho - ly ground is burn - ing,

all a - round your world there are voi - ces sing - ing.
all a - round your world men and wo - men ris - ing, sing-ing
all a - round your world there is faith re -

Chorus

Ho - ly,— ho - ly,— ho - ly is— the Lord.— Ho - ly,—

ho - ly,— ho - ly is— the Lord.—

2a Meditation on renewal

Son of Man, in your presence our inner spirits burn,
your ways of power and love we long to learn.

Son of Man, whose glorious grace we cannot earn,
renew and fix in us the hope of your return.
Amen

3

All I am
(Each perfect gift has come from you)

Capo 2 (D)

Andy Flannagan

Worshipfully

yet I cling tight - ly. And I pray, O Lord,
for this world's sto - ry. We have no o -
but this road is nar - row; it leads me on -

Last time to Coda

re - lease my grip, so I give glad - ly.
- ther pur - pose than to give you glo - ry.
- ly to a cross, Lord, I will fol -

Bridge

For I am bro - ken, but I am cho - sen, for you have spo -

- ken grace to me. Yes, I am bro - ken, but I am cho -

D.C. Coda

- sen, for you have spo - ken grace to me. - low.

13

All of my lifetime

4

Dave Clifton
& Noel Richards

Simply

1. All of my life - time you have been call - ing,
2. If I should rise on wings of the morn - ing,

though I was far from you. E - ven in dark - ness
fly to a dis - tant shore, still you would find me,

your love has found me, I could not hide from you.
your hand would guide me, now and for - e - ver more.

Search me, all my deep-est long-ings; know me, all I think and do.

Lead me, I will walk be-side you; show me what's good and true,

may I be more like you.

5

All who are weary
(Come)

Unhurried

Benjamin Sternke

come,— come to the foun-tain;— from the well of sal-
come, be found by the Fa-ther,— let his ra-diance—

va-tion, come and drink deep. Run, run, run in-to his
burn a-way all your shame. Run, run, run in-to the

shel-ter,— and find your life's great-est peace.
ri-ver,— im-merse your

2. All who are heart in-to the flood of grace. Come and find rest,

rest for your— soul.— Come and find rest, rest for your—

(continued over...)

17

_soul.___ Come and find peace,_____ peace like you've ne - ver

known;___ come and find___ rest,___ rest for your___ soul.___

5a From Bethlehem to Nazareth

From Bethlehem to Nazareth,
From Jordan to Jericho, from Bethany to Jerusalem,
from then to now,
Come, Lord Jesus.

To heal the sick, to mend the broken-hearted,
to comfort the disturbed, to disturb the comfortable,
to cleanse the temple, to liberate faith from convention,
Come, Lord Jesus.

To carry the cross, to lead the way,
to shoulder the sin of the world and take it away,
Come, Lord Jesus.

Today, to this place, to us,
Come, Lord Jesus.

John Bell Copyright © WGRG, Iona Community, G2 3DH

6

As high as the heavens
(The voice of hope)

Lara Martin

Expressively ♩ = 74

Verse

1. As high as the hea-vens are a-bove the earth, so high are your ways to mine.

Ways so per - fect they ne - ver fail me, I

know you are good all the time! And through the storm

yet I will praise you, de - spite it all yet I will sing; through

good or bad yet I will wor - ship, for you re-main the same King of

(continued over...)

Lara Martin (Abundant Life Ministries, Bradford, England). Copyright © 2002 Thankyou Music/Adm. by worshiptogether.com songs
excl. UK & Europe, Adm. by kingswaysongs.com tym@kingsway.co.uk. Used by permission.

7

Amazing grace
(My chains are gone)

Words: John Newton (1725-1807)/John P Rees (1828-1900)
& Edwin Othello Excell (1851-1921)
Arr. and additional choruses
by Chris Tomlin & Louie Giglio

This song is recorded on the Spring Harvest New Songs 'Wonderful Saviour' album

free, my God, my Sa - viour has ran-somed me. And like a

flood his mer - cy reigns, un-end-ing love, a - maz - ing grace.

1.,3.

3. The Lord My chains are
4. The earth

Coda

be for - e - ver mine.

23

8

Are you ready, ready, ready?
(R u ready?)

Godfrey Birtill

Fast rock 'n' roll style

8a Prayer of hope
Based on Romans 8

Loving Father God, source of all grace and truth, help us as we pray in hope:

Let us set our minds on the things of you 'Abba, Father God,' that we may be filled with peace, life and love. Let us cry out to you 'Abba, Father God,' for those in need, knowing that we are all your children – co-heirs with Christ in his suffering and glory. Let us cry out to you 'Abba, Father God' for the whole of creation that longs for your healing and restoration.

Let us be confident in the promise that you have set before us; that all things work together for the good of those who love you. Let us be empowered by your Holy Spirit and willing to defend the hope that you have put within our hearts. Let us know with full assurance that nothing we can ever encounter will be able to separate us from the love of God shown to us in Jesus Christ our Lord. **Amen**

9   As I sing my songs of praise to you

Stuart Barbour

As I sing my songs of praise to you, I know that you are here; search my heart and know the trou-bles I have held. For in this place of your ac-cep-tance, and for-give-ness of the past is where the things that come a-gainst me can-not stand. You're the rea-son for the morn-ing, you're the light that shines the way, I will

Pour out your Spi - rit, Lord, let it fall.—

You're the God and— my friend.

As one in Christ the Lord

10

LOVE UNKNOWN

Words: Timothy Dudley-Smith
Music: John Ireland
Arr. David Peacock

1. As one in Christ the Lord his glo-ries here pro-claim, ex-alt his ho-ly word, his e-ver-last-ing name: let love and praise u-nite our pow'rs for we are Christ's and Christ is ours.

2. On him our hope is set, whose cross is strong to save; nor shall our hearts for-get that emp-ty Eas-ter grave: with him we rise, our sins for-giv'n, to share with him the life of heav'n.

3. Be ours to use a-right the gifts of thought and mind, in scrip-ture take de-light, and God's ap-pro-val find: till through the Spi-rit and the word there stands re-vealed the liv-ing Lord.

4. Whom Je-sus calls he sends, to make his mer-cies known: am-bas-sa-dors and friends, the he-ralds of his throne. His word of truth and life de-clare: with all the world his go-spel share.

5. To fol-low Christ our aim, in him to stand com-plete, that all may hear his name and bow be-fore his feet: the faith to keep, the race to run, and hear at last the Lord's 'Well done!'

11 As morning dawns and evening fades
(Your name)

Capo 3

Paul Baloche
& Glenn Packiam

Steadily

1. As morn - ing dawns and eve - ning fades, you in - spi - re
2. Je - sus, in your name we pray, come and fill our

songs of praise___ that rise from earth___ to touch___ your heart,___ and
hearts to - day.___ Lord, give us strength___ to live___ for you___ and

glo - ri - fy___ your name.___ Your name___ is a
glo - ri - fy___ your name.___

Your name___ is a

strong and migh - ty tow - er. Your name___ is a

shel - ter like— no o - ther. Your name,— let the

na - tions sing— it loud - er, 'cause no - thing has— the pow - er to save—

1.,3. **Last time to Coda**

— but your name.—

2.

D.S. al Coda **Coda**

Your name— —

12

Beauty unspoken

Steadily

Paul Oakley

1. Beau-ty un-spo - ken, glo-ry un-chan - ging,_____
   - ness, one with the Fa - ther,_____

ma - ker of the stars a - bove._____ God un-cre-a-
the be - gin - ning and the_ end._____ Lif - ter of bur-

- ted, made your-self no - thing;_____ car-ry - ing the cross for_ love._
- dens, bruised and for-sa - ken,_____ Je-sus Christ the sin-ner's_ friend.

Chorus

A   E/G♯   F♯m7+4   A   E/G♯   F♯m7+4

Thank you, God,_____ thank you, God,_____

13

Behold the Lamb
who bears our sins away
(The communion song)

Thoughtfully

Keith and Kristyn Getty
& Stuart Townend

Verse

1. Be - hold the Lamb who bears our sins a - way, slain for us:
2. The bo - dy of our Sa - viour, Je - sus Christ, torn for you:
3. The blood that clean - ses ev - 'ry stain of sin, shed for you:
4. And so with thank - ful - ness and faith we rise to re - spond

and we re - mem - ber the pro - mise made that all who come in faith find for -
eat and re - mem - ber the wounds that heal, the death that brings us life, paid the
drink and re - mem - ber he drained deaths' cup that all may en - ter in to re -
and to re - mem - ber our call to fol - low in the steps of Christ as his

Chorus

give - ness at the cross. So we share in this bread of life, and we
price to make us one. As we share in his suf - fer - ing, we pro-
ceive the life of God. *(Last chorus)*
bo - dy here on earth.

drink of his sa - cri - fice, as a sign of our bonds of peace
claim: Christ will come a - gain! And we'll join in the feast of heav'n

around the table of the King.
around the table of the King.

To end

13a Proclamation to a broken world
Based on Isaiah 43 & 55

The congregation may turn to face outwards to symbolise God's proclamation to the world.

Come, you who are thirsty:
Eat, drink and be filled, at no cost to yourselves.
Come, you who have wasted your lives:
Come to the Lord, live and be satisfied.
Come, you who are seeking for meaning:
Turn to the Lord, receive mercy and be healed.
Come, you who are overwhelmed:
come and be carried to safety,
come and be rescued from the flames.
Come, you who are fearful:
you are precious and honoured;
the Lord has paid for your release; the Lord has set you free.
Come, you who long for the past:
forget nostalgia:
the Lord has for you a new future, it is springing up right now.
Come to the Lord: your Creator and your Saviour calls you;
look for him while he is close to you; call on him while he is near.
Turn to him and find life. Amen.

Copyright © John Leach

14 Beneath the cross

Keith & Kristyn Getty

Gently & thoughtfully

1. Be - neath the cross of Je - sus, I find a place to
   neath the cross of Je - sus his fam - ily is my
   neath the cross of Je - sus, the path be - fore the

stand; and won - der at such mer - cy that
own; once stran - gers chas - ing self - ish dreams, now
crown, we fol - low in his foot - steps where

calls me as I am. For hands that should dis -
one through grace a - lone. How could I now dis -
pro - mised hope is found. How great the joy be -

card me, hold wounds which tell me 'Come'. Be - neath the cross of
ho - nour the ones that you have loved? Be - neath the cross of
fore us to be his per - fect bride. Be - neath the cross of

This song is recorded on the Spring Harvest New Songs 'Wonderful Saviour' album

Je - sus my un - wor - thy soul is won.
Je - sus see the chil - dren called by God.
Je - sus we will glad - ly live our

2. Be -
3. Be -

3.
lives.

14a   Psalm of salvation

A river of praise will pour from our lips
to our matchless, our wonderful God.
For you, only you, were able to save us,
to liberate us from sin's hold.

Thanks to you we are free, unbound and absolved,
no longer weighed down and in darkness.
Our punishment is paid, our debt has been settled
in the agony Christ endured on the cross.

Death is defeated, hope is restored
as Christ was raised up and stands honoured.
For in him is life, abounding with promise –
a new life, a new destiny, a new purpose.

Our past is redeemed, our present, transformed
and our future is sealed and assured.
It's all by God's hand that we now can stand
in the presence of the Almighty God!

15 Blessèd are the people

With an 'r n b' feel

Godfrey Birtill

1. Bles-sèd are the peo - ple who know the joy - ful sound.___
2. Bles-sèd are the peo - ple who know that God is good.___

1.

2.

Hear the sound of the trum - pets, hear the
Who know the joy of for-give - ness, all their

voice of the Lord,___ it's the year of God's fa - vour and
sins washed a - way.___ Hear the sound of the gos - pel, it's still

sal - va - tion joy.___ Bles-sèd are the peo - ple who know the joy - ful
break-ing the chains.___ Bles-sèd are the peo - ple who know that God is

is breath-ing hope in our hearts— once a gain.

15a   Prayer of confidence

God our Saviour,
You are the hope of all the ends of the earth and the seas
and of all that is in between
In your name we put our trust, for your name is good.

Open our eyes that we may be enlightened in the promise
to which you have called us.
In your name we put our trust, for your name is good.

Open our hearts that we may be blessed by the riches
of Christ's glorious inheritance in the saints.
In your name we put our trust, for your name is good.

Open our lives that we may be made secure
by your incomparably great power for us who believe.
In your name we put our trust, for your name is good.

May we live for ever to your praise and honour.
Amen

16 Break our hearts and break our silence

(Raise your voices)

With passion

Andy Flannagan

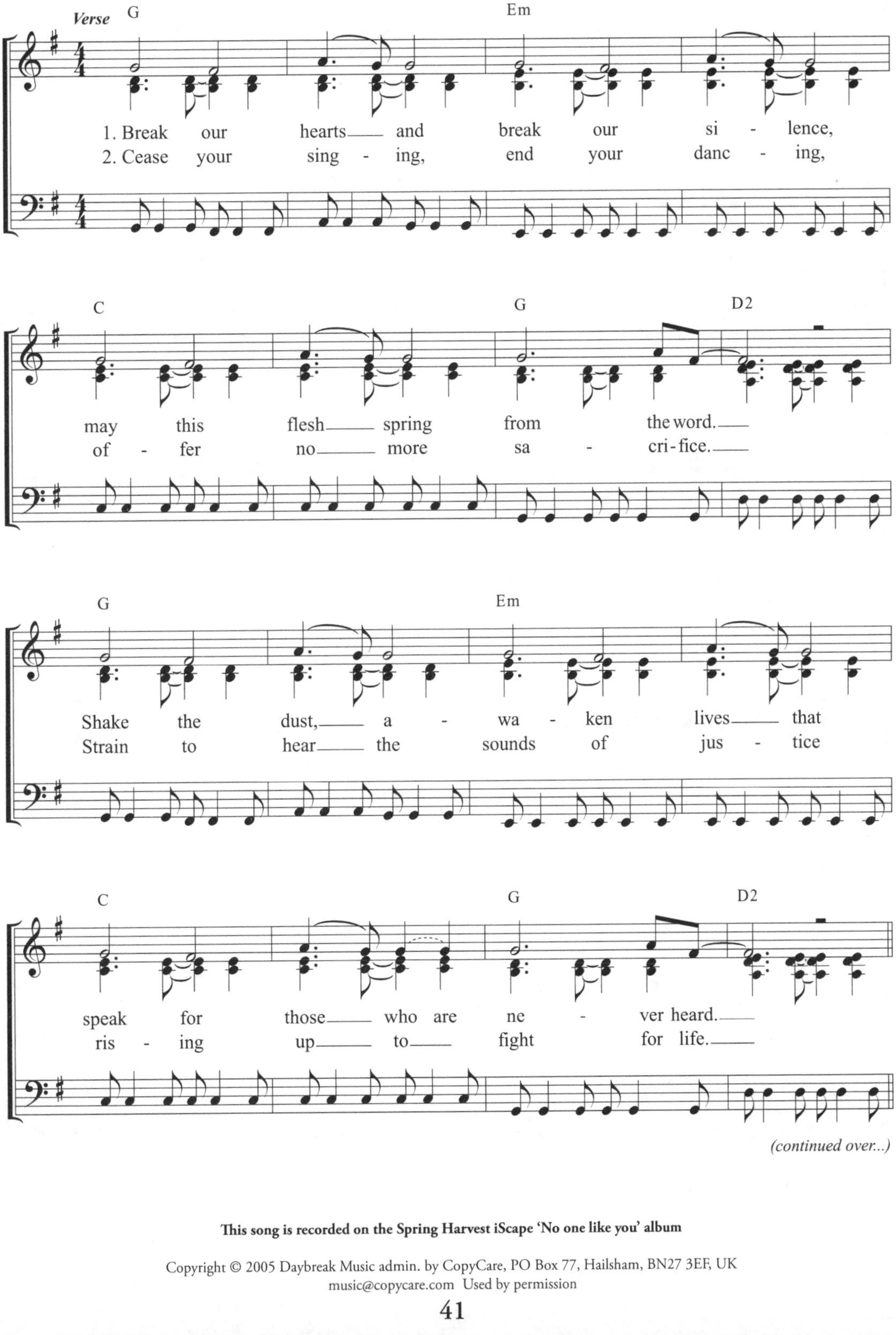

Verse
G Em
1. Break our hearts — and break our si - lence,
2. Cease your sing - ing, end your danc - ing,
C G D2
may this flesh — spring from the word. —
of - fer no — more sa - cri-fice. —
G Em
Shake the dust, — a - wa - ken lives — that
Strain to hear — the sounds of jus - tice
C G D2
speak for those — who are ne - ver heard. —
ris - ing up — to — fight for life. —

(continued over...)

This song is recorded on the Spring Harvest iScape 'No one like you' album

17

Bring heaven to earth, Lord
(We are blessed)

Capo 3 (D)

Andy Flannagan

Moderate 4

1. Bring hea-ven to earth, Lord, bring peace where there's fear;
   home to the home-less, bring keys to the chained;
   jus-tice to pro-fit, bring pa-tience to growth;

bring life where there's death, Lord, bring
bring worth to the pur-chased, and
bring wis-dom to pro-gress, like

joy in these tears. Bring love where there's lust, Lord, bring
touch to the shamed. Bring flesh from your word, Lord, bring
food for the soul. Bring free-dom from debt, Lord, an

hope where there's pain; bring rest where there's cha-os, bring
truth where there's spin; bring risk where there's safe-ty, and
end to ex-cess; bring clos-er your king-dom by

(continued over...)

C(A) Gm(Em) B♭(G)

— the change— you pro - mised. We are freed—

Last time to Coda ⊕ **1.,3.** **2.**

F(D) C(A) B♭(G)

— to be— your hands,— O— God.—

2. Bring
3. Bring

Bridge C(A) B♭(G) C/E(A) B♭/D(G)

Lord,— we cry— out to— you, change— the at - mos - phere;—

C(A) B♭/D(G) C/E(A) F(D) B♭(G) **1.**

breathe— new life—— in all— who ga - ther here.—

2. *D.S.* ⊕ *Coda* F(D)

We are blessed

46

18

Come and see
what our God has done

Andrew J. Booth
& Jessica Witmer

Steady rock 4

1. Come and see what our God has done,—— how he turned the sea in-
2. Come and see what our God has done,—— how he made the lame to
3. Come and see what our God can do,—— what he's done be-fore, he'll

to dry land.—— And all the peo-ple passed—— through the wa-ters,
walk and run.—— How he made—— blind—— eyes to see,——
do for you.—— He makes his e-ne-mies bow down be-fore him,

hemmed—— in—— by a cloud of fire.——
how he came to set the cap-tives free.——
come all you na-tions of the world a-dore him.

Chorus

Praise—

(continued over...)

he's the same — God — to-day and for-e-ver. He is faith-ful to a

thou-sand ge-ne-ra-tions,— what he's done be-fore he'll do a-gain.

D.S. al Coda ⊕ **Coda**

Praise— —God.———

18a   Signs of hope and glory

Covenant God, we have been unfaithful in our promises to you
Yet we see signs of hope and long to see your glory come on earth
Covenant God, we have not served you with our whole hearts
Yet we see signs of hope and long to see your glory come on earth
Covenant God, you are the source of forgiveness, power and love
We see your signs of hope and long to see your glory come on earth

May your Kingdom come in our lives
May your Kingdom come in our world
In Christ we pray. Amen

19 Come O Fount of every blessing

NETTLETON

Celtic feel

Words: Robert Robinson (1735-1790)
Tune: American trad.
Arr. David Peacock

1. Come, O Fount of ev-'ry bles-sing, tune my heart to sing your grace; streams of mer-cy, ne-ver ceas-ing, call for songs of loud-est praise: songs of__ God's a-bun-dant trea-sure, sung by__ an-gel tongues a-bove, songs that tell the bound-less mea-sure of my

mem-ber God's great mer-cy: by his help I've safe-ly come; and I know he will not fail me, but will sure-ly bring me home. Je-sus__ sought me when a stran-ger wan-d'ring far a-way from God, and, to res-cue me from dan-ger, shed for

grace I am his debt-or— dai-ly I this thought re-new! Let that grace, Lord, like a fet-ter bind my wan-d'ring heart to you. Prone to__ wan-der, Lord, I feel__ it, prone to__ leave the God I love! Take my heart, O take and seal it, seal it

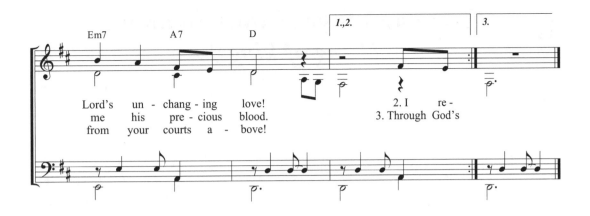

Lord's un - chang - ing love!
me his pre - cious blood.
from your courts a - bove!

2. I re -
3. Through God's

19a   We will not walk

Lord God forgive us when we follow the ways of the world
the desires of our bodies
the flights of our imaginations
our pleasure-driven hearts.
We will not walk in the way of sin
But the way your Spirit leads us

Forgive us when we journey down the road of worldliness
of pleasure and possession
of acquiring and increasing
and needing to have.
We will not walk in the way of sin
But the way your Spirit leads us

Encourage us to tread on the path of truth and goodness
following Christ's way of loving and serving
and worship through all we do
We will not walk in the way of sin
But the way your Spirit leads us

Guide us in the way of the Kingdom of heaven
that gives us hope for tomorrow and forever
for the sake of his honour and glory.
We will not walk in the way of sin
But the way your Spirit leads us

20 Come on lift your voice in praise
(King of kings)

Moderate salsa feel

Terl Bryant, Jules Bryant
& Noel Robinson

1. Come on, lift your voice in praise, ce-le-brate the high-
2. Tell-ing of his migh-ty works, bring an of-f'ring that's

- est name;— his words are true and ne-ver fail.—
- of worth;— stand on ev-'ry word just like he said.—

Hear his word and grow in faith,—
Shout for joy,— sing to the King;—

see his glo-ry, re-ceive his grace;— he reach-es out—
strike the drum,— be-gin to sing:— de-clare him—

to ev - 'ry race._____ King of
_ the King__ of kings._____

kings, Je - sus__ is__ King: thy king - dom come,__

_ ev - 'ry bo - dy sing._____

1.,3.   *2.*   *D.C.*

4.

Come praise the name of Jesus

21

MORNING LIGHT

Music: George Webb
arr. David Peacock
Words: Christopher Idle

Unhurried ♩ = 110

1. Come, praise the name of Je - sus for all his gra - cious
pow'rs, our on - ly God and Sa - viour who makes his good - ness
ours; he calls us to his king - dom, the Lord of life and
death,___ to see his face in glo - ry and know him now by

vir - tue and his wis - dom, en - du - rance, self con -
trol, his god - li - ness and kind - ness, his love which crowns them
all. This is his ro - yal na - ture that we are called to
share,___ his robe of per - fect beau - ty that we are giv'n to

see his shin - ing splen - dour in ev - 'ry sun - less
place where Christ, the light of na - tions, ap - pears in truth and
grace. Trans - fi - gured by his like - ness we make the vi - sion
known,___ re - flect - ing in our fa - ces the ra - diance of his

King of grace in - spires us to love him more and
more, to grasp our hope more firm - ly and make our call - ing
sure. Christ Je - sus, Lord and Sa - viour, to this dark world you
came;___ and for the dawn of hea - ven, we praise your ho - ly

faith.
wear.
own.
name.

2. His
3. We
4. The

21a   We pray for those
Based on Isaiah 40

We pray for those bowed down by worry,
imprisoned by guilt, disfigured by shame.
O God, comfort your people.
Carry them close to your heart.

We pray for those desperate for justice,
those crying out for vindication,
and for those speaking for the voiceless.
O God, comfort your people;
Carry them close to your heart.

We pray for those who live in ignorance,
those who have given their hearts to false idols,
those who do not know and have not heard that the Lord reigns.
O God, comfort your people;
Carry them close to your heart.

We pray for the sick, the weak, the powerless;
those who stumble and fall, those whose minds or bodies fail them.
O God, comfort your people;
Carry them close to your heart.

We pray for those close to death, those very aware of human frailty,
and those who watch with them.
Comfort, comfort your people O God;
Speak tenderly to us, renew our strength,
and come to reign over us as judge and king. Amen

22

Come see a vision

Steady

Steve James

1.,4. Come see a vi-sion for all hu-man kind; whose hearts were so cold, whose
2. Come see the King in his glo-ry ar-rayed; ma-jes-tic in power, his
3. Come see the life that re-stores and re-makes, the hope of the world that

eyes were so blind; now join-ing the ran-somed, re-stored and re-fined
name shall be praised who stoops from the heav-ens to save those he made,
breaks through the grave: for the judge of the earth is the Je - sus who saves,

sing to the Lord of our lives, it's a glo-ri - ous love.

23 Could it be that God could move
(*Would you move*)

Capo 3(G)

Andy Flannagan

(continued over...)

To record or not to record?

With easier access to studios and home recording software it is not uncommon to record and produce albums of 'home grown' songs. Even with the wider availability of studios, recording still requires a significant outlay of time and money and needs to be seriously considered. When does a song move from personal expression to something that needs to be made more widely available?

Before recording your songs, think about these questions;

- Is the song a story of a personal journey?
- Has it been written with your church community in mind?
- Have the lyrics been checked by your pastor or other suitable theologian?
- Does the song reflect a wider theme that can be seen across the Kingdom of God globally?

Once these have been answered, think about if and why it needs to be recorded and for whom it is intended. Some songs are written in the deep recesses of a personal journey, carved out with God often in difficult times. Being able to express this through song can be an amazing way to explore the depths of what God is doing. Even though the resulting song may be a cry from the heart it is not necessarily a cry from everyone's heart.

Maybe you are skilled in writing songs that reflect what God is saying to your community. Singing these songs is a corporate declaration of where God is taking you together and an encouragement to everyone. Recording them for your own community's use may be immensely beneficial but beyond that may not be appropriate.

Imagine a song which has an integrity of its own and expresses the depths of your journey with God in both the melody and the way it is sung. This is something worth aiming for whether it is heard by thousands or only One.

Kate Silber
www.nexustrust.co.uk

24 Crucified to save me

Steady 4 ♩ = 63

Chris Gasson

Verse

1. Cru - ci - fied___ to save___ me,
2. You walked a path___ of bro - ken - ness,___

cru - ci - fied___ to wash___ me clean;___
you walked the path___ that was___ my own.___

your love and life___ were poured___ out,
I'll take my cross___ and fol - low you___

giv'n that I___ could be___ set free.___
and de - mon - strate___ the love___ you've shown.___

Blood and wa - ter flowed, spilt that I might know your___ love.
Lead me to that place where I see your grace and___ love.

Words and Music: Copyright © Chris Gasson/RESOUNDworship.org admin. by The Jubilate Group
4 Thorne Park Road, Torquay TQ2 6RX, UK copyrightmanager@jubilate.co.uk Used by permission

Chorus
Take me back to the cross,___ take me back, show me more___ ___ of the cost.___ Let your Spi - rit come and turn my eyes to see your per - fect sa - cri - fice.___

Show me more___ of
I'm hum - bled by___ this

Cal - va - ry,___ oh, lead me to___ that___ place.___
my - ste - ry,___ I bow be - fore___ such___ grace.___

63

Dance, dance
(Joy is in this place now)

25

Words: John Newton (1725-1807)
Music & words adaption: Tim Hughes

With a strong rhythm

1. Dance,— dance,— e - v'ry-bo-dy dance, e - v'ry-bo-dy sing, for joy— is in this place now. Dance,— dance,— e - v'ry-bo-dy dance, e - v'ry-bo-dy sing, for joy—— is in this place now.
2. Shout,— shout,— e - v'ry-bo-dy shout, e - v'ry-bo-dy scream, for joy— is in this place now. Shout,— shout,— e - v'ry-bo-dy shout, e - v'ry-bo-dy scream, for joy—— is in this place now.

And e - v'ry-bo-dy dance now.——
Yeah, joy—— is in this place now.——

26

Even though I walk
(You never let go)

Capo 2 (A)

Matt & Beth Redman

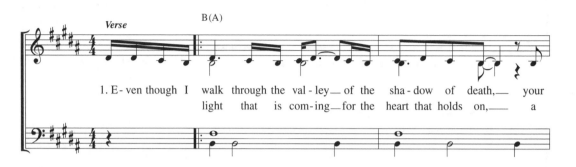

1. E-ven though I walk through the val-ley— of the sha-dow of death,— your
light that is com-ing—for the heart that holds on,— a

per-fect love is cast-ing out fear.——— And e-ven when I'm
glo-rious light be-yond all com-pare.——— And there will be an

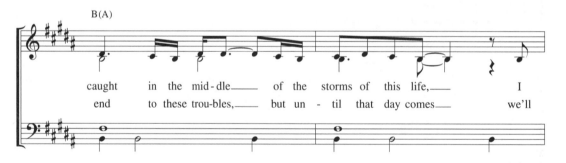

caught in the mid-dle——— of the storms of this life,—— I
end to these trou-bles,—— but un-til that day comes—— we'll

won't turn back, I know you are near.—— —
live to know you here on the earth.——

This song is recorded on the Spring Harvest New Songs 'Wonderful Saviour' album

Everlasting

27

Steadily

Sue Rinaldi
& Caroline Bonnett

1. E - ver - last - ing, e - ver true, all cre - a - tion sings to you. E - ver faith - ful, liv - ing Lord, let the sound of praise be heard. Je - sus, you are all that I am liv - ing for and all that I be - lieve is in you. Je - sus,

2. Ne - ver chang - ing, awe - some God. Sing the glo - ry of the Lord. E - ver lov - ing, Ho - ly One, I will praise what you have done.

all that I am liv - ing for, and all that I be - lieve is in you.

28

Everlasting God
(Yesterday, today and forever)

Capo 3 (D)

Rock style

Vicky Beeching

ci - ful and good, so good.

Chorus

Yes - ter - day, to - day and for - e - ver, you are the same,

you ne - ver change. Yes - ter - day, to - day and for - e - ver,

Last time to Coda

you are faith - ful and we will trust in you.

2.

We will trust in you,

(continued over...)

71

we will trust— in you,—— in you.—

Yah - weh,— God un - chan-ging. Yah - weh,—

— firm foun - da - tion. You are da - tion.

29 Every good and perfect gift
(You'll be there)

Becky Frith
& Leah Broomfield

Ev-'ry good and per - fect gift comes from your hand.

Count - less mer - cies I've re - ceived un - de - served by me.

Ev - 'ry new day, the sto - ry un - folds of your grace in my life. Each day the same, you ne - ver change and for - e - ver you'll reign.

(continued over...)

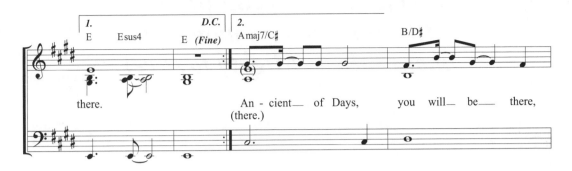

there.

An - cient— of Days, you will— be— there,
(there.)

faith - ful— and true, you will— be— there, mer - ci - ful— and just,

you will— be— there, be - gin - ning and— end.— You'll be

30 Everyone needs compassion
(Saviour, he can move the mountains – Mighty to save)

Steady 4

Reuben Morgan
& Ben Fielding

1. Ev-'ry-one needs com-pas - sion, love that's ne - ver-fail
2. So take me as you find— me, all my fears and fail

- ing; let mer - cy fall on— me.—
- ures, fill my life a - gain.—

Ev'ryone needs for-give - ness,— the kind - ness of a sa -
I give— my life to fol - low— ev - 'ry-thing I be-

- viour; the hope of na - tions.—
lieve in, now I sur - ren - der.—

This song is recorded on the Spring Harvest New Songs 'Wonderful Saviour' album

31

Every time that I'm broken
(You are my Rock)

Steadily

Gavin Dines
& Andy Flannagan.

breath I breathe____ I wor-ship you.____ You are__ my__ rock,__

__ you are__ un-chang-ing, I__ will wor - ship__ you. You build__ me up__

__ when I__ am bro-ken, so__ I'll wor - ship__ you. For__ my heart__

__ it lies__ in pie-ces, but it's in____ your__ hands. You're the pot-

ter, would__ you mould__ me to__ your_____plan? Ev - 'ry__

(continued over...)

80

32
Firstborn of Mary

With a bounce

John L. Bell

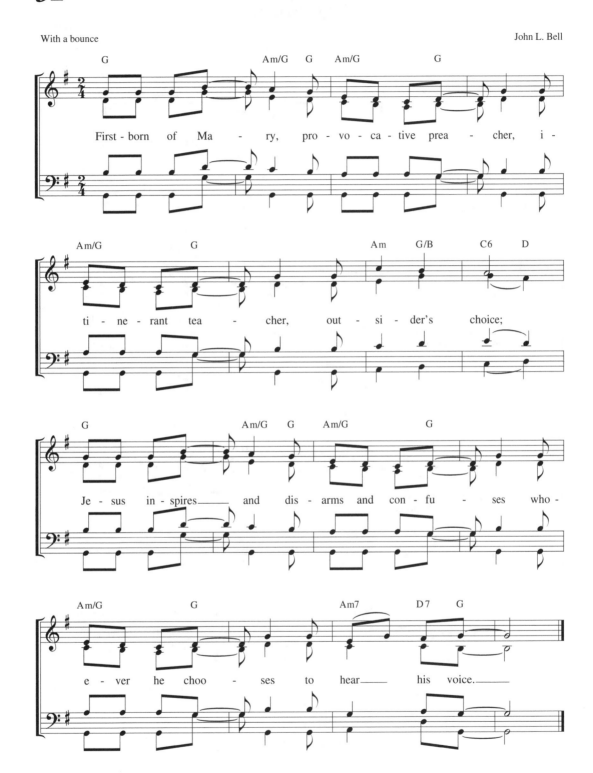

First-born of Ma - ry, pro-vo-ca-tive prea - cher, i-ti-ne-rant tea - cher, out-si-der's choice; Je-sus in-spires and dis-arms and con-fu - ses who- e-ver he choo - ses to hear his voice.

33 Father of life
(Anchor)

Isaiah 9:6
Psalm 74:16

Geraldine Latty
& Andrew Small

Verse

1. Fa - ther of life, you are my hope, hope that is stea - dy, hope that is sure. E - ven when ques - tions stir in my mind, your coun - sel and hope an - chor my life. an - chor my soul.

2. Al - migh - ty God, you are my peace, peace that is so - lid, peace that is real. E - ven as storms seem to con - trol; your whole - ness and peace an - chors my faith.

3. Won - der - ful Lord, you are my joy, joy as my pur - pose, joy as my goal. Here at the cross I wit - ness to - day: your fo - cus on joy

(Small notes 2nd verse only)

Chorus
It is you, Je - sus, it's you: Lord of the day and the

night. I trust in you,＿ for your ways are true:＿ God o - ver all,＿ I be -

long to you. Your ho - ly name it

an - chors me; it's all in your name, all in your name. Your all in your

name.＿＿＿ It is

34

For every song
(You are)

Capo 2(G)

Ben Cantelon, Tim Hughes
& Nick Herbert

Steadily, with strength

1. For ev-'ry song, for ev-'ry breath,
   word, full of grace,

for ev-'ry good and per-fect gift you give.
for all the stead-fast pro-mi-ses you make.

For ev-'ry night, for ev-'ry day, for the glo-
For the cross, for new life, for the beau-

-ry of the earth, we will say: You are
-ty of your sa - cri-fice.

35

Forgive us Lord
(Hear our song)

Andy Flannagan

1. For- give us, Lord, for what we've done and what we've left un- done.
2. A- wa- ken me from where I sleep, this bliss is ig- no- rance.
3. We will not leave you on your own at the mar- ket's mer- cy.
4. Our God in pain, re- veal a- gain the depth of what

— un- done. / — no- rance. / — ket's mer- cy. / — you feel.

Hear our song ris- ing to you. All this wrong ig- nites our shame. No more build- ing earth-

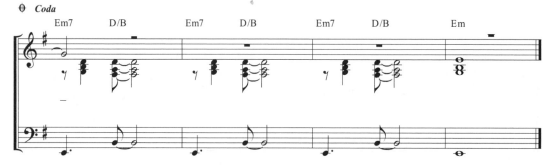

sis-ter's cries?

35a   Glory to Christ!

Group A   Do you remember the wedding at Cana,
Where Jesus took water and turned it to wine?

Group B   *Yes, we remember it: glory to Christ!*
He is the Vine, the one true Vine.
And do you remember the loaves and the fish,
How Jesus fed thousands from one boy's food?

Group A   Yes, we remember it: glory to Christ!
He is the Bread, the Bread of life.
And do you remember the man born blind,
Whose eyes Jesus opened, letting him see?

Group B   *Yes, we remember it: glory to Christ!*
He is the Light, the Light of the world.
And do you remember, at Lazarus' tomb,
The word that brought Lazarus back from the dead?

Group A   Yes, we remember it: glory to Christ!
He is the Resurrection, the Life.

All   **We will remember all of these things.**
We will remember them: glory to Christ!

Songs of justice

Throughout the Old Testament, it is proclaimed that God's reign is based on the dual foundations of justice and righteousness. When we speak or sing of God's passion for justice, and the implications of that in our own lives, we are not just paying lip service to another noble cause that the church is becoming involved in, but prophetically speaking of the nature of the King and his coming Kingdom.

Often songs based around justice themes will have sprung from a particular context. For instance the song 'Forgive us Lord' (no.35) was written after experiencing the negative legacy of Britain's empire and the West's continuing culpability in Bangladesh. It is often helpful to explain these contexts, perhaps with still images or video material. Try to integrate these songs into your regular 'canon' rather than always making them a special event.

Avoid the temptation that all worship leaders face to simply 'give the people what they want'. Often justice-themed songs do not provide the 'warm fuzzy, holy moment' that can sometimes seem to be the goal of modern worship. Sometimes you have to hold your nerve, believing that the place that includes anger, confusion, grief and sorrow is just as valid a place to be in worship as happy, content and victorious. Avoid the temptation to use another song to 'get everyone up' again!

The words of Amos chapter 5:21–24 speak powerfully enough on their own, but they might hit even closer to home if they read like this…

'I hate your festivals. I cannot stand your worship events. Even though there are thousands of people, and the PA could cause an earthquake, I will not accept them.
Even though the band is fantastic, and you have the best worship leader in the world, I have no regard for them. Do you think I care who sells most CDs? Do you think I care what the 'cool new song' is? Away with this individualised, feel-good soundtrack of iPOD "worship".
I'm listening online to another channel. It's called Justice and Righteousness, and it's arriving on a broadband connection that is wider than you could ever imagine.
That's what I want to hear. I know when someone's playing MY song.'

God invites us to be part of the 'bringing in' of his Kingdom of justice and righteousness. In modern worship contexts there are often opportunities to turn our prayers and singing outwards such as crying out for the poor of the world. This may be from a place of compassion, having been broken by images or stories, but this may also be from a place of anger, having been informed of the injustices in our global economic system. Jesus engaged his heart both in weeping for a dead friend and his family, and in throwing over the tables of the money-changers in the temple. We need to listen for God's heartbeat, that it might become our own, so that his compassion and anger pulses through our veins as we sing, that the words of Ezekiel chapter 11 would be proved true – *'I will give them an undivided heart and put a new spirit in them; I will remove from them their heart of stone and give them a heart of flesh.'*

Andy Flannagan www.andyflan.com

See the Thematic Index on page 293 for more examples of justice songs in this book.

36

From the dawn of time
(Unchanging)

Moderately

Pete & Nicki Sims

Verse

Emaj7   B   A   Emaj7   B   A

1.) From the dawn__ of time,__   to the end__ of days,__
      Age to age__ the same,__   your love ne - ver fails,__
2.) Time - less, e - ver true,__   faith - ful e - ver more,__
      Stead - fast to__ the end,   through - out e - ter - ni - ty,__

Emaj7   B   A   Emaj7   B   A

     you will e - ver be__   un - chang - ing.__

Bridge

C#m7   F#m7   A

You are__ the rock,__ where__ my feet__ are__ se - cure.__

B   C#m7   F#m7   A

You ne - ver change,__ al - ways con - stant__ and sure.__

Chorus

God, you are my hope,—— you are my strength,—

you are my joy—— for - e - ver. — for - e - ver.—

Un - chang - ing.——

91

37
From the highest of heights
(Indescribable)

Capo 3(B♭)
With strength

Laura Story
Add. lyrics Jesse Reeves

1. From the high-est of heights to the depths of the ___ sea, ___
   From the co-lours of fall to the fra-grance of ___ spring, ___
2. Who has told ev-'ry light-ning bolt where it should ___ go,
   Who i-ma-gined the sun and gives source to its ___ light,

cre-a-tion's re-veal-ing your ma-je-sty.
ev-'ry crea-ture u-nique in the song ___ that it sings.
or seen hea-ve-nly store-hous-es la-den with snow?
yet con-ceals it to bring us the cool-ness of night?

All ex-claim-ing: In-de-scri-ba-ble, un-con-tain-a-ble,
None can fa-thom:

you placed the stars in the sky, and you know them by ___ name: ___ you are a-maz-ing,

93

38
Glory, glory all around
(Jesus is)

Gary Clarke
& Peter Wilson

39

God in my living
(Be my everything)

Tim Hughes

Capo 4(G)
Gently building

Additional choruses:
You are everything . . .
Jesus, everything . . .

40

God of justice
(We must go)

Tim Hughes

1. God of jus-tice, Sa-viour to all,___ came to re-
2. To act just-ly e-ve-ry day.___ Lov-ing mer-

-scue the weak and the poor,___ chose to serve___ and not___ be___ served.
-cy in___ ev-'ry way.___ Walk-ing hum-bly be-fore you, God.

Je-sus,___ you have called us.___
You have shown us___ what you re-quire.___

Free-ly we've re-ceived, now free-ly we will give. We must go, live to feed the

hun-gry, stand be-side the bro-ken. We must go,___ step-ping

Last time to Coda ⊕

for - ward, keep us from just sing - ing, move us in - to ac - tion, we __ must

1. Bb(G) *D.C.* *2.* Bb(G) *D.S.* *3.* Bb(G)

go. __ go. __ We must go. __

Bb(G) C(A) F(D)

Fill us up and send us out, __ fill us up and send us out, __

Bb(G) *1.,2.* C(A) *3.* C(A) *D.S. al Coda*

fill us up and send us out, __ Lord. __ Lord. __ We must

⊕ *Coda* Bb(G) F(D)

go. __

41 God of the mountains
(Creation praise)

Moderately

Sue Rinaldi,
Caroline Bonnett & Steve Bassett

1. God of the moun-tains, God of the light in the
2. Wis-dom of a - ges, light in the

— sea, God of the hea-vens, God of the
— dark, home for the out-cast, friend of the

of e - ter - ni - ty. God of the
peace for the heart: friend of the

fu - ture, God of the past,
lone - ly, strength for op - pressed,

42

Great are you Lord
(Awesome is the Lord most high)

Fast rock

Chris Tomlin, Jesse Reeves,
Cary Pierce & Jon Abel

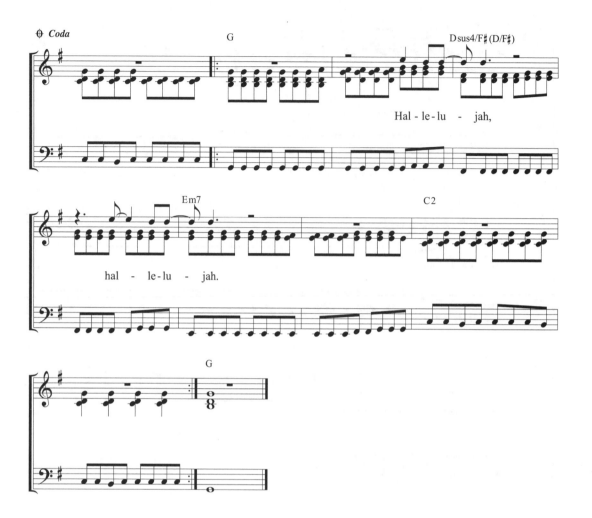

Coda

Hal - le - lu - jah,

hal - le - lu - jah.

42a   Strong love
Based on Psalm 62

Strong love upholding me
Strong love supporting me
Strong love surrounding me
My God
My Rock
Strong love

43

Great is your faithfulness
(Your grace is enough)

Matt Maher
Additional lyrics: Chris Tomlin

1. Great is your faith - ful - ness, O God.
   you lead us by still wa - ters in - to mer - cy,
2. Great is your love and jus - tice, God.
   you lead us in the song of your sal - va - tion,

You wres - tle with the sin - ner's heart,
and no - thing can keep us a - part.
You use the weak to lead the strong,
and all your peo - ple sing a - long.

So, re - mem - ber your peo - ple, re - mem - ber your

chil - dren, re - mem - ber your pro - mise, O God.

(continued over...)

This song is recorded on the Spring Harvest New Songs 'Shine' album

In the lyrics under the music: -ered in____ your love.____ Your grace is e - nough____ for____ me,____ for____ me.

43a   Your word
Based on Isaiah 40–55

In the empty deserts of lonely isolation
Your word speaks of belonging in community.
In the desolate silence of the white noise of living
Your word makes sense of past, present and future.
In the midst of the vastness of an unexplored universe
Your word affirms your astonishing greatness.

In the heart-rending pain of a bruised and broken world
Your word promises comfort, strength and security.
In the anonymity of crowds a billion strong
Your word addresses us directly and personally.
In the gnawing guilt no busyness can expunge
Your word offers absolute forgiveness and acceptance.

In the hunger for wholeness and purpose in life
Your word invites us to the feast of eternity.
In a culture which idolises riches and brute force
Your word is the powerful weakness of suffering love.

Great is your faithfulness
(Unchanging)

44

Chris Tomlin

1. Great is your faith-ful-ness, great is your faith-ful-ness.
2. True are your pro-mi-ses, true are your pro-mi-ses.
3. Wide is your love and grace, wide is your love and grace.

You ne-ver change, you ne-ver fail, O God.

Chorus

So, we raise up ho-ly hands to praise the Ho-ly One; who was, and is, and is to come.

Yeah, we raise up ho-ly hands to praise

the Ho - ly One; who was, and is, and is to come.

You were, you are, you will al - ways be. You were, you are,

you will al - ways be. So, we raise

45

He is here

Capo 2 (D)

Paul Baloche
& Brian Doerksen

(continued over...)

46

He made the heavens
(Come let us worship)

Ken Riley

1. He made the hea- vens and they shine his glo- ry,
2. He made the world in all its count- less won- der,

he moves the sun a- cross the sky; so in- com- pa- ra- ble, the
com- posed the song cre- a- tion cries: our God, in- cre- di- ble, im-

star of morn- ing, ra- di- ant in light.
mor- tal, Sa- viour Je- sus Christ.

Chorus

Come, let us wor- ship, come let us
His ways are migh- ty, right- eous and

(continued over...)

wis - dom— are yours, all—— yours.

yours, all yours.— Lord—— has done.

46a   The thread of hope

In the beginning, Lord God, you made the world
and declared it good;
you formed man and woman
and blessed them with life and hope.

When your people found themselves trapped,
whether enslaved in Egypt or despairing in Bablyon,
you reached down to rescue them,
rekindling their hope.

You have done this for us, too,
through Jesus, your Son: born among us,
dying for our forgiveness, raised for our righteousness,
ascended for our security and our hope.

**And now you are making all things new,
shaping the people of heaven
and building the age to come
where all things will be good for ever.
Great God, our Creator, our Liberator, our Hope,
we honour you.
Amen**

47 Higher than the stars could be
(Forever over us)

With energy

Trè and Tori Sheppard,
Mark Prentice, Paul Baker, Jonny Ravn,
Steve Evans & Nathan Dantzler

Verse

1. High-er than the stars could be, fur-ther than the end-less seas, far be-yond to-mor-row
   I was lost, my heart a-sleep, you gave ev-'ry-thing for me. When I called you ans-wered;

2. You're so much more than just be-lief, King of all, but friend to me. You have all of my heart,
   One day ev-'ry-one will see, bro-ken hearts will know your peace; there'll be no more sor-row,

(2,3.&4.)

4th time to Mid-Section ⊕   *Bridge*

your love car-ries me.   You're ev-'ry-thing I need.
you have res-cued me.
you have cap-tured me.
we will all be free.

Chorus

Je - sus, for-ev - er

o - ver us you have writ - ten love.

Sa - viour, you have res - cued us;

for - ev - er o - ver us with love.

1. A

(continued over...)

117

Song writing for congregations – Part 1

The two fundamental pillars

The two fundamental pillars in scripture for the songs we sing are – rich in scriptural meaning and easily singable. These are the two primary goals of the words and music in congregational song or hymn writing.

It starts with the congregation

Many of the greatest songs ever written are not singable by congregations. Those of us who are musicians always tend towards songs that are most musically interesting, or sound best on a recording or even at a major event with a professional band and this really doesn't feed the congregations we lead. Let's use the congregation as our guide rather than musicians as they ultimately determine what is good – and if they are unengaged and are just spectators we have missed the point. Truly radical worship is where people of every generation, cultural background, social status and stage in life can sing melodies together as a family to their Creator and Redeemer. It is not where there is some spectacular performance – we can get that in concerts, television and DVD's – and by comparison it's really not that radical.

A songwriter's best friend is...his pastor

Pastors and musicians don't exactly have a reputation of being friends. I think one of the reason there are so many good songs written in UK is because of the great relationships between visionary pastors and their musical directors – always work with your pastor – both in what songs to write, in listening to their sermons and in writing songs for occasion. Also use their theological input in the writing process and have them check the songs both for emphasis and accuracy. This can really help form deep, powerful relationships.

More 'Song writing for congregations' tips can be found in Part 2 on page 265

Keith Getty

www.gettymusic.com

48
Holy, holy, holy God
(Holy God)

Capo 3 (G)

Brian Doerksen

Moderately

Holy, holy, holy God.

Holy, holy,

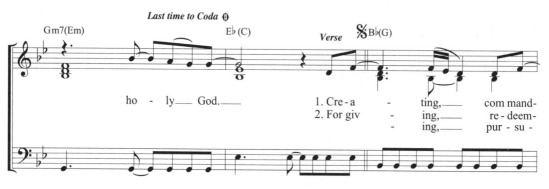

ho - ly God.

1. Cre - a - ting, com mand-
2. For giv - ing, re - deem-
   - ing, pur - su -

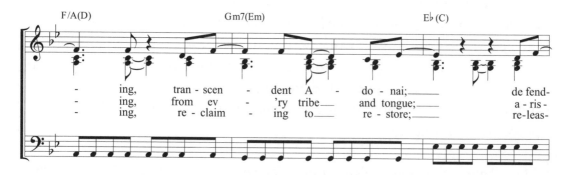

- ing, tran - scen - dent A - do - nai; de fend-
- ing, from ev - 'ry tribe and tongue; a - ris-
- ing, re - claim - ing to re - store; re - leas-

- ing love,___ de-stroy – ing sin, the War – ri – or – di - vine._
- ing first,___ the nail – scarred Lamb, sal - va – tion's cham - pi - on._
- ing hearts,___ trans-form – ing lives, the Li – on's migh - ty roar._

3. Ro - manc - –

48a   See my Servant
From Isaiah 52 & 53

See my Servant, says the God of hope,
wounded, scarred and broken.

Many shall see and be astonished:
nations, startled and shocked,
their leaders staring and speechless.
He was wounded to bring wholeness.

Come my servant, says the God of hope,
wounded, scarred and broken.

Go into a world which is battered and bruised,
its peoples hungry and without hope.
Walk with my people, and bring wholeness.

God of hope, you sent Jesus, wounded, scarred and broken,
to walk with us.
**Send us now, your wounded, scarred and broken church,
to bring wholeness and hope.**

49 I am not skilled to understand
(My Saviour, my God)

Rock 4 (straight 8's)

Aaron Shust

1. I am not skilled to un - der - stand
   deed, bring

what God has willed, what God has planned;
Christ died to save me, this I
my strength, my so - lace from this

read,
spring,

I on - ly know at his right hand
and in my heart I find a need
that he who lives to be my King

stands one who is my
for him to be my
once died to be my

Sa - viour.
Sa - viour.
Sa - viour.

2. I take him at his word and

This song is recorded on the Spring Harvest New Songs 'Wonderful Saviour' album

Bridge

2.,3.

That he would leave his place on high and come for sin-ful man to die.

You count it strange, so once did I, before I knew my Sa-viour.

Chorus

My Sa-viour loves, my Sa-viour lives, my Sa-viour's al-ways there for me. My God he was,

Last time to Coda

my God he is, my God he's al-ways gon-na be. My Sa-viour loves,

(continued over...)

al - ways gon na be.

3. Yes, liv - ing, dy - ing, let me

al - ways gon - na be.   My Sa - viour lives,— my Sa - viour loves,— my Sa - viour lives,—

— my Sa - viour loves,— my Sa - viour lives.—

50

I offer up to you
(*True praises*)

Mark Beswick, Howard Francis
& Clive McKinley

I of-fer up to you prai-ses from my heart, that they may be in truth the per-fect sa-cri-fice. To show my gra-ti-tude for all the things you do, I just want to give true prais-es from my heart. Lord, I give to you true prai-ses from my heart.

51 I will always love the Lord
(Honour the Lord)

Capo 2 (G)

Graham Kendrick
& Trè Sheppard

1. I will al - ways love the Lord——— with all of my heart;
2. I will al - ways trust the Lord——— with all of my heart;

I will al - ways sing his praise——— with all of my strength.
I will place my hope in him——— with all of my strength.

Through the bad—— times and the good——————— I've proved his love——
He has been—— my hid - ing place——————— when - e - ver - I feel——

(continued over...)

of the poor,— of the lost—— and the weak;— and our shame—— falls a-way— as our fa-

ces shine— with his love.———— *(Leader)* So ho-nour the Lord—

— with me. *(Leader)* Ho-nour the Lord———— with— me.
(All) We ho-nour you, Lord. *(All)* We

(Leader) Ho-nour the Lord———— with me.
ho-nour you, Lord.——

If ever I should falter
(With your grace)

Martyn Layzell
& busbee

Capo 3 (G)

(continued over...)

This song is recorded on the Spring Harvest New Songs 'Shine' album

When all a-round me is sha - king__ in this world,__ oh yeah.__

U - pon your so - lid foun - da - tion__ I stand firm.__

If e - ver I__ should fal -

53 In the face of present sufferings

DIM OND JESU

Words: Martin E. Leckebusch
Music: Robert Lowry (1826-99)

1. In the face of pre-sent suf-f'rings,— Chris-tians let us not for-
2. Count-less so-lar sys-tems wres-tle— with frus-tra-tion and de-
3. We who taste the Spi-rit's first-fruits— still are groan-ing in-ward-

get: there are great-er glo-ries com-ing— than we have en-vi-saged
cay till the cli-max of the a-ges,— when their chains are swept a-
ly, yearn-ing for our full re-demp-tion, for our bo-dies' li-ber-

yet! All cre-a-tion waits, ex-pec-tant,— till God's han-di-work is
way. Now, we sense the pains of child-birth— which the cos-mos has to
ty. To be God's per-fec-ted chil-dren— is the hope by which we

known: till the chil-dren of his pro-mise— to a watch-ing world are shown.
bear; then the free-dom we in-he-rit— all the u-ni-verse will share.
live; pa-tience, bro-ther, sis-ter, pa-tience:—what he pro-mised, God will give.

In the name of the Father
(Our God saves)

54

Paul Baloche
& Brenton Brown

Moderately

In the name of the Fa-ther, in the name of the Son, in the name of the Spi-rit, Lord, we_____ come. We're ga-thered to - ge-ther to lift up your name, to call on our Sa-viour, to fall on your grace.

In the name of the grace. Hear the joy-ful__ sound of our of-fer-ing as your saints bow__ down, as your

(continued over...)

This song is recorded on the Spring Harvest New Songs 'Wonderful Saviour' album

55

Jesus Christ, Perfect Love
(Perfect Love)

Geraldine Latty & busbee

Thoughtfully

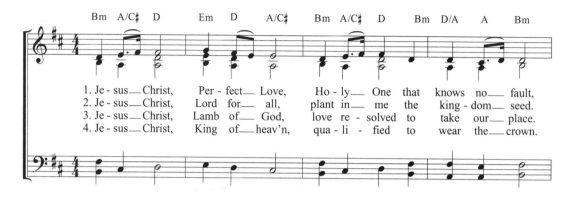

1. Je-sus—Christ, Per-fect—Love, Ho-ly—One that knows no—fault,
2. Je-sus—Christ, Lord for—all, plant in—me the king-dom—seed.
3. Je-sus—Christ, Lamb of—God, love re-solved to take our—place.
4. Je-sus—Christ, King of—heav'n, qua-li-fied to wear the—crown.

screen my—thoughts, make me—clean, know the—mo-tives of my—heart.
Search me,—Lord, when I'm—found look-ing—on-ly to my—needs.
Who can—write or de-scribe all of—your self-giv-ing—grace?
In your—face, ra-diant—grace draws us—clo-ser to your—throne.

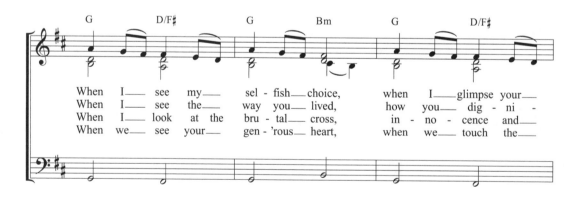

When I—see my—sel-fish—choice, when I—glimpse your—
When I—see the—way you—lived, how you—dig-ni-
When I—look at the—bru-tal—cross, in-no-cence and—
When we—see your—gen-'rous—heart, when we—touch the—

55a You called your disciples

Lord Jesus Christ,
you called your disciples to go forward with you
on the way to the cross.

Since you first walked that road
countless millions have followed you.

In all that we do as your disciples,
save us from false familiarity with your journey.
May we never presume to step into your shoes,
but make us small enough to fit our own,
and to walk in love and wonder behind you.
Amen

56 Jesus, hope of the nations
(Hope of the nations)

Strong rhythm

Brian Doerksen

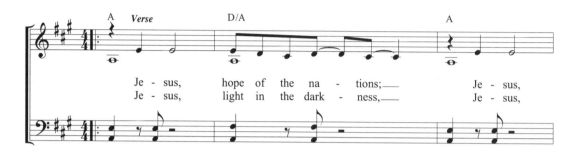

Je - sus, hope of the na - tions;___ Je - sus,
Je - sus, light in the dark - ness,___ Je - sus,

com - fort for all___ who mourn,___ you are___ the source___ of hea -
truth in each cir - cum - stance,___ you are___ the source___ of hea -

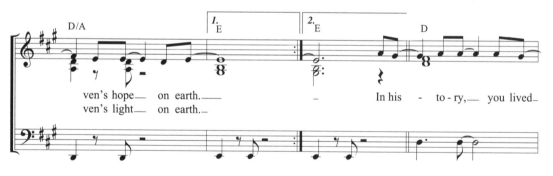

ven's hope___ on earth.___
ven's light___ on earth.___

In his - to - ry,___ you lived___

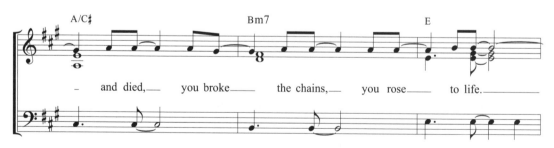

— and died,___ you broke___ the chains,___ you rose___ to life.___

57

Jesus, lead me
(Fix my eyes)

Moderately

Andrew J. Booth

1. Je - sus, lead___ me; Je - sus, trans-form___ me.
2. Fa - ther, heal___ me; Fa - ther, re - store___ me.
3. Spi - rit, teach___ me; Spi - rit, com - fort me.

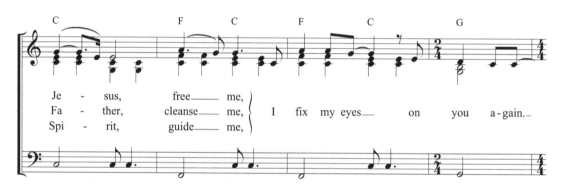

Je - sus, free___ me,
Fa - ther, cleanse___ me,   I fix my eyes___ on you a - gain.___
Spi - rit, guide___ me,

Chorus

Whom have I___ but___ you,___

who can lead___ me through?___ You have the words of life;

speak your truth to me, speak your truth to me.

1.,2.

Last time

Speak your truth to me, speak your truth to me.

57a   Jesus Christ, we greet you!

Jesus Christ, we greet you!
Your hands still have holes in them,
your feet are wet from the dew;
and with the memory of our names
undimmed by three days of death you meet us,
risen from the grave.

We fail to understand how;
we puzzle at the reason why.

But you have come;
not to answer our questions,
but to show us your face.

**You are alive
and the world can rejoice again.
Hallelujah!
Amen**

58

Jesus my King,
my wonderful Saviour
(Wonderful Saviour)

With a steady rhythm

John Millard Harris (1867-1934)
Words adpt. & music: Andy Bromley

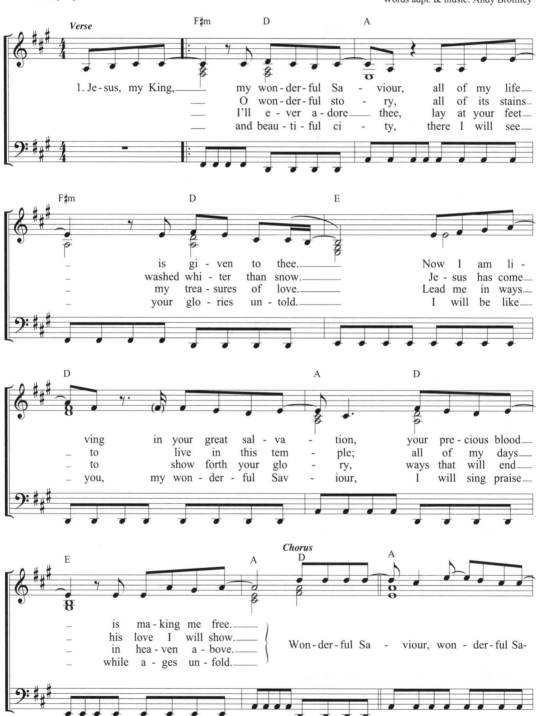

1. Je-sus, my King,— my won-der-ful Sa - viour, all of my life— is gi - ven to thee.— Now I am li - ving in your great sal-va - tion, your pre-cious blood— is ma-king me free.—

— O won-der-ful sto - ry, all of its stains— washed whi - ter than snow.— Je-sus has come— to live in this tem - ple; all of my days— his love I will show.—

— I'll e - ver a-dore— thee, lay at your feet— my trea-sures of love.— Lead me in ways— to show forth your glo - ry, ways that will end— in hea-ven a-bove.—

— and beau-ti-ful ci - ty, there I will see— your glo - ries un - told. I will be like— you, my won-der-ful Sav - iour, I will sing praise— while a - ges un - fold.

Chorus

Won-der-ful Sa - viour, won-der-ful Sa-

This song is recorded on the Spring Harvest New Songs 'Wonderful Saviour' album

- viour, you are so near,——— so pre-cious to me.——— Won-der-ful Sa-

- viour, won-der-ful Sa - viour, my heart is filled—— with prai-ses to thee.—

1. - 3.

2. Free - dom from sin——
3. Je - sus my Lord,——
4. When in that bright——

58a   A prayer for joy and hope
From John 2

Loving God,
your Son turned water into wine at the wedding;
transform our lives,
make us glad by his presence with us,
and fill us with joy and hope;

through Jesus Christ our Saviour.
Amen

59

Jesus, you are mercy
(Jesus, you are worthy)

Brenton Brown

Je - sus, you are_____ mer-cy,_____ Je - sus, you are_____ jus-tice, Je - sus, you are_____
_ wor-thy,_____ that is what you_____ are. You died a-lone_____ to_____
_ save me,_____ you rose so_ you could raise_____ me;_____ you did all this_ to make_____
_ me_____ a cho-sen child_____ of God. Wor-thy is the Lamb that once was slain_
_ to re-ceive all glo - ry, pow'r and praise,_____ for with your blood you

Last time to Coda ⊕

pur - chased us for God: Je - sus, you are wor - thy, that is what you

1. — are. Je - sus, you are — are.

2. Per - fect sa - cri -

fice, crushed by God for us, bear - ing in your hurt all that I — de - serve. —

— Mis - judged for my mis - deeds, you suf - fered si - lent - ly, the on - ly guilt - less

D.S. al Coda

man in all of hi - sto - ry. — How wor - thy is the

(continued over...)

145

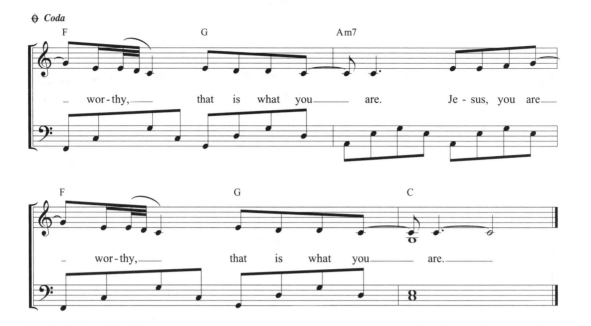

⊕ *Coda*

wor-thy,_____ that is what you_____ are. Je - sus, you are_____

wor-thy,_____ that is what you_____ are._____

59a   Prepare the way for God
From Isaiah 4: 3–5

Build a road in the wilderness
and straighten desert paths.
Prepare the way for God!

Raise up all the valleys
and flatten all the hills.
Prepare the way for God!

Make a way through rough terrain
and smooth down all the bumps.
Prepare the way for God!

Soften hearts as hard as iron
and open bolted doors.
Prepare the way for God!

Bring together those at odds
and let forgiveness set them free.
Prepare the way for God!

Break down barriers of race and class
and welcome those who don't fit in.
Prepare the way for God!

60

Jesus, your beauty is filling this temple
(Holy river)

Sue Rinaldi
& Caroline Bonnett

♩ = 88

Verse

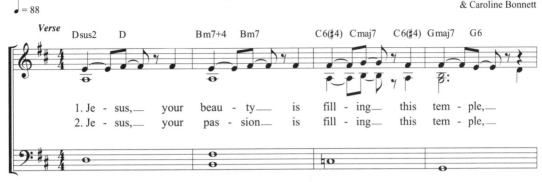

1. Je - sus, your beau - ty is fill - ing this tem - ple,
2. Je - sus, your pas - sion is fill - ing this tem - ple,

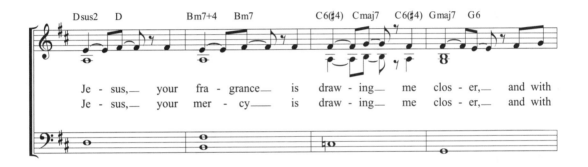

Je - sus, your fra - grance is draw - ing me clos - er, and with
Je - sus, your mer - cy is draw - ing me clos - er, and with

ev - 'ry step I take you lead me in - to this ho - ly place
ev - 'ry step I take you lead me in - to a world that aches,

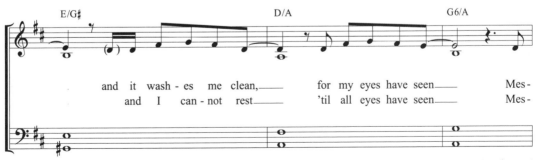

and it wash - es me clean, for my eyes have seen Mes-
and I can - not rest 'til all eyes have seen Mes-

(continued over...)

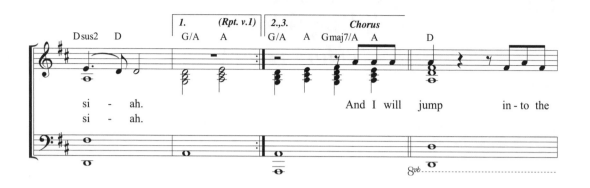

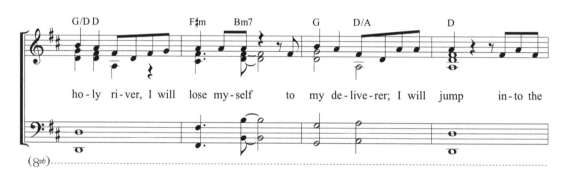

149

61

Joy is the theme of my song
(Beautiful news)

Rocky

Matt Redman

Verse

Joy is the theme of my song, and the beat of my
you showed the pow'r of your cross, and your great sav-ing

heart, and that joy is found_____ in you._____ For
love, and my soul woke up_____ to you._____

I heard your beau-ti-ful news,_____ grace so a-maz-ing, so true._____

Chorus

Shout it out,___ let the peo - ple sing,___ some-

-thing so pow-er-ful should shake the whole wide world.

Make it loud,— make it loud - er still,— Sa - viour, we're sing-ing now to

Last time to Coda ⊕ **1.**

cel - e - brate your beau - ti - ful news.—

2.,4. ***D.S.***

— Shout it out,— let the peo -

3.

There's a God who came down—
showed the world his a - maz -

— to save,——
- ing grace.—

(continued over...)

151

62
King of angels, King of saints
(Praise you)

Paul Oakley

With energy

1. King of an - gels, King of saints, King of all cre - a - tion praise. King of lost and King of found, King who wore my thor - ny crown. Cru - ci - fied to set me free, King of glo - ry, now my eyes can see your ma - je - sty.

2. King of sun - shine, King of rain, King of all my wak - ing days. King in joy and King through pain, you will al - ways be the same. Sing a - loud, my soul a - wake, sing of his un - fail - ing love and grace, all my days.

Chorus

And I praise you, I praise you, I praise

(continued over...)

62a   Prayer of preparation

God, our hope, as we gather now to worship you,
fill us with anticipation and prepare us by your Spirit.

Be the first thoughts in our hearts
and may we be conscious that you will direct our time together.

Fully reliant on you, may we be strengthened for service,
nourished by the bread of life and transformed in purpose.

In the name of Jesus Christ, we ask this.
Amen.

63 Let the earth resound

Keith Getty
& Stuart Townend

Chorus

King im-mor-tal, faith-ful God, crowned with splen-dour, rich in love. Let the hea-vens and the earth re-sound with songs of praise to you.

grace.
free.
praise:

2. Let the you.
3. Let the

63a   Renew our strength
From Isaiah 40

Restoring and renewing God,
you have measured the waters
and marked off the heavens;
you have scooped up the dust
and weighed the mountains.
When we faint and fall with weariness and worry,
renew our strength, lift us up,
and set us on our journey again,
that we may travel in hope
and serve you wherever you have called us;
through Jesus Christ, your Servant.
Amen

64
Lord, we have seen
(Shine)

Capo 1 (G)

Matt Redman

Steady 4

Verse

Lord, we have seen ___ the ris-ing sun ___ a-wa-ken-ing ___
the stars and moon, ___ see how they shine,

___ the ear-ly dawn, ___ and we're ris-ing up to give you praise.
___ they shine for you, ___ and you're call-ing us to do the same.

1.
___ Lord, we have seen ___

2.
___ So we rise ___

___ up with a song, ___ and we rise ___ up with a cry, ___ and we're giv-

- ing you our lives. ___

Chorus

We will shine ___ like stars ___ in the u-
___ so bright ___ with your praise,

Last time to Coda ⊕

-ni-verse,___ hold-ing out___ your truth___ in the dark - est place.___ ⎱ We'll be
_ O God,___ and de-clare___ your light___ to this bro - ken world.___ ⎰

liv-ing for your glo - ry, Je-sus, we'll be liv-ing for your glo - ry.

1. *D.C.* *2.,4.* *D.S.* *3.*

Lord, we have seen___ We will burn___ Like the sun___

_ so ra-diant-ly,___ send-ing light___ for all to see,___ let your ho -
plod-ing in - to life,___ like a su - per - no-va's light,___ set your ho -

1.,3. *2.* *(1st line)*

- ly church a - rise._____ Ex- Like the sun___
- ly church on fire._____

(continued over...)

159

65

Lord, you promised

Matt Osgood

1. Lord, you pro-mised if we speak in faith,___ we'll see the moun-tains move,___
pro-mised if we pray in faith,___ we'll see the sick re-stored___

___ your pow'r will make our path - ways straight.___ Lord, you
___ as we call on your might - ty name.___ Lord, in

pro mised if we live by faith___ we'll do the things you did,___ all for our
ev - 'ry - thing you will pre - vail, so we can trust your word___ for it will

Fa ther's praise.___ Yet, in our lives we don't see___ all you___ have prone - ver fail.___

(continued over...)

mised; help us to be-lieve, help us to be-lieve.

Chorus

Lord, we're call-ing out, in-crease our faith,

so that your king-dom's pow'r will be dis-played in all we

do and not just what we say. Lord, would you re-lease

your gift of faith, we pray. 2. Lord, you

(Fine)

1. D.C. 2.

Mid section

No-thing is im-pos-si-ble—— for you,—— Lord, no thing is im-pos-si-ble—

— for you.—— May our doubt-ing hearts be - lieve—— the truth—

— that no-thing is im-pos-si - ble—— for you.—— We're

66

Mercy to the broken-hearted
(Everything changes)

Capo 1 (D)

Mildred Rainey
& Kathryn Scott

1. Mer - cy to — the bro - ken-heart - ed, life for those — who grieve, —
2. Bless - ing to — the poor — in spi - rit, grace for all — in need, —

joy to those — whose dreams — are sto - len, im - pri - soned souls re - leased. —
sight to those — who live — in dark - ness, — in - no - cence re - deemed. —

When you come, ev-'ry-thing chan - ges; — when you speak, e-ven the dark-

- ness hides. — When you step in - to our frail - ty, Je - sus,

(continued over...)

this is the king-dom come,___ this is the king-dom.___

ev-'ry-thing chan-ges,___ ev-'ry-thing chan-ges,_

ev-'ry-thing chan - ges,___

ev-'ry-thing chan - ges.___

67

My life flows on in endless song
(How can I keep from singing?)

Robert Lowry (1826-99)
Arr. John L. Bell

Capo 3(D)

Firmly ♩ = 80

1. My life flows on in end-less song a-bove earth's la-men-
2. Through all the tu-mult and the strife, I hear that mu-sic
3. What though the joys and com-forts die? The Lord my Sa-viour
4. The peace of Christ makes fresh my heart, a foun-tain e-ver

ta-tion.— I catch the sweet, though far off, hymn that hails a new cre-
ring-ing; it finds an e-cho in my soul, how can I keep from
liv-eth. What though the dark-ness round me close? Songs in the night he
spring-ing.— All things are mine since I am his! How can I keep from

Chorus

a-tion.—
sing-ing?—
giv-eth.— No storm can shake my in-most calm while to that rock I'm
sing-ing?—

cling-ing.— Since love is Lord of heav'n and earth, how can I keep from sing-ing?—

68 My hope is built on nothing less

Capo 3(D)

Words: Edward Mote (1797-1874)
Music: William B. Bradbury (1816-1868)
arr. Robert Critchley

Steadily

My hope is built on no-thing less than Je-sus' blood and
(2.) dark-ness veils his love-ly face, I rest in his un-

right-eous-ness. My hope is built on no-thing less than Je-sus' blood and
chang-ing grace. In ev-'ry high and stor-my gale, my an-chor holds with

1st time only

right-eous-ness. My right-eous-ness. My hope is built on
in the veil. His oath, his co-ve-
(3.) he shall come with

no-thing less than Je-sus' blood and right-eous-ness. I
nant, his blood sup-ports me in the whelm-ing flood. When
trum-pet sound, oh may I then in him be found. Dressed

169

69

My soul finds rest in God alone
(Psalm 62)

Aaron Keyes
& Stuart Townend

Thoughtfully

1. My soul finds rest in God a-lone, my rock and my sal-va-tion; a
soul finds rest in God a-lone a - mid the world's temp-ta-tions; when
set my gaze on God a-lone and trust in him com-plete-ly; with

fort-ress strong a-gainst my foes, and I will not be sha-ken. Though
e-vil seeks to take a hold I'll cling to my sal-va-tion. Though
ev-'ry day pour out my soul and he will prove his mer-cy. Though

lips may bless and hearts may curse, and lies like ar-rows pierce me, I'll
rich-es come and rich-es go, don't set your heart up-on them; the
life is but a fleet-ing breath, a sigh too brief to mea-sure, my

fix my heart on right-eous-ness, I'll look to him who hears me.
fields of hope in which I sow are har-vest-ed in hea-ven. O
King has crushed the curse of death and I am his for-e-ver.

This song is recorded on the Spring Harvest New Songs 'Wonderful Saviour' album

To repeat

praise him, hal-le - lu - jah, my de - light and my re - ward; e-ver - last - ing, ne ver
fail - ing, my Re - deem er, my God.

2. My—
3. I'll—

Last time

70

Not angels, nor demons
(I belong)

Capo 3 (D)

Mildred Rainey
& Kathryn Scott

1. Not an-gels, nor de-mons, no pow'r on earth or hea-ven.
2. Not hard-ship, nor hun-ger, no pain or depth of sor-row.

Not dis-tance, nor dan-ger, no trou-ble now or ev-er.
Not weak-ness, nor fail-ure, no bro-ken dream or pro-mise.

Bridge

No-thing can take me from your great love, for-e-ver this truth re-mains.

(Last time D.S. to repeat Bridge)

Chorus

I be-long, I be-long to you. I be-long,

173

71

O God of righteousness
(I am persuaded)

Robin Mark

Steadily ♩ = c.70

1. O God of right-eous-ness,____ O God of
sua-ded nei-ther death nor

love, your word is per-fect and____ your ways are just. When dark-ness
life, nor pow'rs on earth or in____ the realms a-bove can e-ver

shades the path____ on which I walk; in you, O Lord, I choose____ to place my
take us from____ your hand, O God, can e-ver se-pa-rate____ us from your

Chorus

I know that my Re-deem-er lives, he is my
trust.
love.
life, my hope,— my strength and pow'r. I know his word will be ful-
filled; his king-dom rule and reign— for-e-ver more. (I know that)

(D.S. 2nd time only)

2. I am per-

175

72

Oh, he is Jehovah
(Come, worship the King)

Moderately

Sonny Lallerstedt

are his— from the— be-gin - ning: his they are— and his they e-ver-

1.,2. *D.C.*

more shall be.

72a   A song of praise for our salvation
Based on St John's Gospel

Thank you, Lord, for your forgiveness, your unfailing mercy
to those who have broken your heart with our rebellion.
Help us to leave our lives of sin.

Thank you, Lord, for new life out of death,
fresh hope out of devastation.
You were the first to rise, but we your children shall follow you.
Take from us our grave-clothes and set us free.

Thank you, Lord, for showing yourself to us.
We were blind, but now we see.
Help us to tell your truth and bring glory to you.

Thank you, Lord, for your provision for us.
You feed us with the bread of life,
the true bread from heaven.
Lord, give us this bread always.

Thank you, Lord, for new hope:
you fill us with the new wine of the Kingdom,
turning our ordinary lives into the sparkling vintage of eternity.
Thank you that you save the best until last. Amen

73

Oh, he's so sweet
(So sweet)

Noel Robinson
& Donna Adoku

This song is recorded on the Spring Harvest Live Worship 'One people' album

filled me with— his glad - ness.— Je - ho - vah Ji - reh, my pro - vi - der.

Je - ho - vah Nis - si, he's my ban - ner. Je - ho - vah Ra - phi,

he's my heal - er, sweet - er than— the hon - ey from the hon - ey comb.—

Coda

— he's so— sweet.

74 O Lord, you've searched me
(At the cross)

Capo 2(D)

Reuben Morgan
& Darlene Zschech

Steady 4

1. O Lord,___ you've searched me,___
2. Your ho - ly pre - sence___
3. You go___ be - fore me,___
4. And when___ the earth fades,___

you know___ my way; even when___ I fail
sur-round - ing me in ev - 'ry sea -
you shield___ my way, your hand up - holds
falls from___ my eyes, and you stand___ be - fore

(1st time D.C. v.2)

you,___
son; I know___ you love me.___
me;
me;

Omit after v.3

I know___ you love me.___ At the cross I bow my

(continued over...)

181

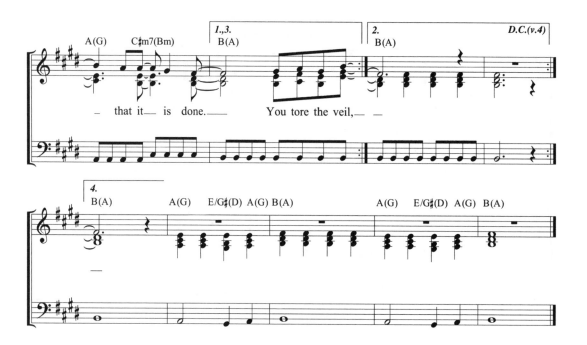

that it— is done.—   You tore the veil,— —

74a   A prayer of confession

For the times when we have abandoned faith
and turned to panic instead:
Holy God, gracious God, forgive us.

For the times when we have lived
as if today was all that mattered:
Holy God, gracious God, forgive us.

For the depth to which we have accepted
the cynicism of our generation:
Holy God, gracious God, forgive us.

For the inadequacy of our proclamation
of the realities of eternity:
Holy God, gracious God, forgive us.

For our contentment in settling for life
that is less than full maturity in Christ:
Holy God, gracious God, forgive us.

Holy God, gracious God, forgive us:
Make us a people of hope and a sign of hope to the world.

Copyright © Martin Leckebusch

One hope

75

Noel Robinson
& Donna Akodu

With strength

Chorus

D/F♯   G2   D/F♯

One hope,— one faith,— one Fa-ther by which— we are saved.—

A   G2   D/F♯   G2

One pur - pose, one mind:—

D/F♯   *After v.3 Chorus to Coda*   A   D

Je - sus is the hope of man-kind.—

(Fine)   **Verse**   Bm

1. We were stran - gers from
2. No more in dark - ness,
3. We are wait - ing for the

(continued over...)

76

O precious sight
(The wonder of the cross)

Capo 1(G)

Vicky Beeching

Steadily

This song is recorded on the Spring Harvest New Songs 'Wonderful Saviour' album

ne - ver lose the won-der, the won-der of the cross. May I see it like the

first time, stand ing as a sin-ner lost. Un-done by mer - cy and left

speech - less, watch ing wide - eyed at the cost.___ May I ne - ver lose the

(Fine)

won - der, the won - der of the cross. 3. Be - hold, the

D.C. al fine

On holy ground
(Join the song)

77

Grandly

Martyn Layzell,
Nathan Fellingham & busbee

1. On ho-ly ground we stand be-fore the King of kings and Lord of all. Where saints have walked this road be-fore, car-ried their cross through hea-ven's door. To the King of hea-ven all the an-gels sing. And I will join the song,

church, lift up your eyes, let your light shine for all man-kind. Hold-ing the flame of truth and life, one heart, one voice, now u-ni-fied. To the King of hea-ven all cre-a-tion sings.

189

On that day

78

Capo 3(G)

Steadily

Geraldine Latty

1. On that day____ there will be no__ in-jus - tice. On that day,__
   (2.)__ there will be no__more sick - ness. On that day,__
   (3.)__ there'll be no he - si - ta - tion. On that day,__

____ there will be no__ more poor.____ So to - day__
____ there will be no__ more death.____
____ ev - 'ry - one will wor - ship you.____

____ I will love,__ I will live,____ I will work, I will__join in____ to see__ your

king - dom come. 2. On that day__ come. Je -

sus, thank you for the price you__paid__ to bring your hea-ven to__ to-day.__

79

Praise is rising
(Hosanna)

With strength

Paul Baloche
& Brenton Brown

Verse G(no3rd)

1. Praise— is ris — ing, eyes— are turn-ing— to you,—
   Hope— is stir — ring, hearts— are yearn-ing— for you,—
2. Hear— the sound— of hearts— re — turn-ing— to you,—
   In your king - dom bro — ken lives—are— made new,—

Csus2   G(no3rd)   *1.*

we turn to you.—
we long for you.—
we turn to you.—
you make us new.—

2.   D   C

'Cause when we see— you, we find strength— to face the day;—

G   D

in your pre - sence all our fears—

are— washed a-way, washed a-way.— Ho - san -
san -

na, ho-san - na,— you are the God— who—saves us,—
na, ho-san - na,— come have your way— a - mong us,—

_ wor - thy of all— our prai - ses.— Ho
_ we wel-come you here— Lord Je - sus.—

Ho -

san - na, ho-san - na. Ho - na.

193

80
Shout the news
(Shout it)

Latin feel

Geraldine Latty

1. Shout the news that God is here;— let them— know, let ev-'ry-one— know. The si - lenced voice can sing a-gain;— let them— know, let ev-'ry-one— know. Shout it - let the sky give— voice.
2. Shout the news that God is here;— let them— know, let ev-'ry-one— know. The ones a - ban-doned found a-gain;— let them— know, let ev-'ry-one— know.
3. Shout the news that God is here;— let them— know, let ev-'ry-one— know. The hope-less can be - lieve a-gain;— let them— know, let ev-'ry-one— know.

Shout it - let the earth ap - plaud. Shout it - let the sea make— noise. For our God is
(2.)
(3.)

with us - for the poor and—— the faint. With us - for the vic - tim—— a-fraid.
with us - for the wor - ker—— un-paid. With us - for the child like—— a slave.
with us - to be good news—— to - day. With us - to be com - fort—— in pain.

With us - for the home - less—— a-gain.
With us - for the land that longs—— for rain. } Yes, our God of love, our God is
With us - to an-nounce a bet - ter way. }

1.,2.
great!

To end
great!——

80a Water of life

Water of life, gushing up,
pouring out, refreshing us,
giving us hope.

Eternal spring, welling up
flowing out, renewing us,
assurance of hope.

Gift of God, promise of life,
here and now, for ever and ever,
eternal hope.

Son of God
(A communion song)

Capo 1(D)

Judy Gresham

♩ = 125

Verse

1. Son of God, we see you here in sou-ve-nirs of grace;
2. Liv-ing bread, e-ter-nal vine, we feed on Christ with-in;

mem-'ries of the wounds you bore, in
faith and hope and love com-bine as

suf-f'ring once em-braced. Lord of all, yet you died,
we re-main in him. By his blood, through the cross,

bruised and scorned, cru-ci fied.
the Son of God gives life to us.

Strength will rise
(Everlasting God)

Brenton Brown
& Ken Riley

This song is recorded on the Spring Harvest New Songs 'Shine' album and on the Spring Harvest Live Worship 'One people' album

83

Stay with me
(Bleibet hier)

Music: Jacques Berthier (1923-1994)

Stay with me, re - main here with me, watch___ and pray;___
Blei - bet hier und wa - chet mit mir. Wa - chet und be - tet,

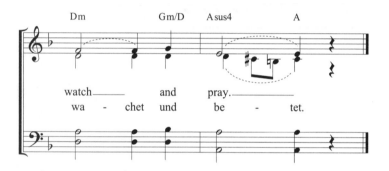

watch___ and pray.___
wa - chet und be - tet.

83a   Losing heart

We've given our hearts to God.
God has our heart.
So if we 'lose heart' for some reason
we will find it again
as we turn to him.

84

Take, O take me as I am

Capo 1 (C)

John L. Bell

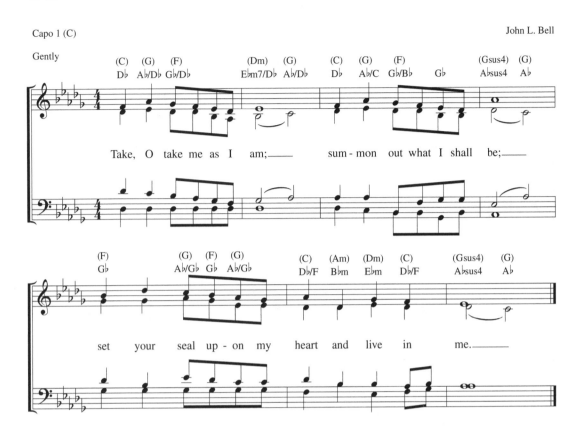

Take, O take me as I am;— sum - mon out what I shall be;—

set your seal up - on my heart and live in me.—

84a   Let the past be past
Based on Isaiah 43:18

Let the past, *be* past in my life
the days have gone; they will never return.
Let me focus on the future
feel a fresh wind of your Spirit –
something new on the horizon.
Let me perceive it;
a new hope, a new day,
let me perceive it.
May I lay down at last, my old strife.

Today – let the past, *be* past in my life.

85

Thank you, Father

Gareth Robinson

Simply

1. Thank you, Fa-ther, for your love for me. Thank you, Fa-ther, for your
2. Thank you, Je-sus, that you died for me. Thank you, Je-sus, that you
3. Thank you, Spi-rit, that you're here with me. Thank you, Spi-rit, that you're

love for me. Thank you, Fa-ther, for your love for me, and I—
died for me. Thank you, Je-sus, that you died for me, and I—
here with me. Thank you, Spi-rit, that you're here with me, and I—

— love you,——— I love you.———
— love you,——— I love you.———
— love you,——— I love you.———

86 The stars dance, the moon glows
(You amaze me)

James Duvall
& Michael Neale

(continued over...)

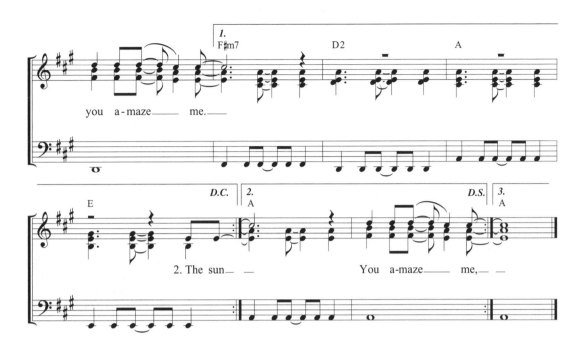

86a God of changeless love
A call to worship

God of changeless love
before you one body we stand.
One voice is raised
as your Kingdom people gather to worship you.
One heart of love pours out
to you the One True God.
One hope of life eternally with you,
where joining with angels we'll worship endlessly;
reconciled to the God of changeless love.

87

The day will come
(Blameless)

Capo 1(D)

Nick Herbert
& John Peters

The day will come— when this world you've made— will sure-ly pass— a-way,— I'll be blame-less— on that— day.—

In that dark hour,— your act— of love— took my guilt— a-way, — I'll be blame-less— on that— day.—

This song is recorded on the Spring Harvest iScape 'No one like you' album

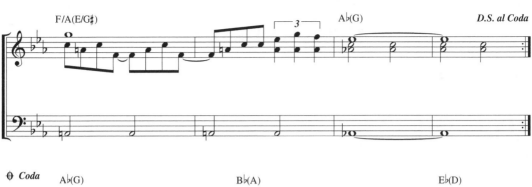

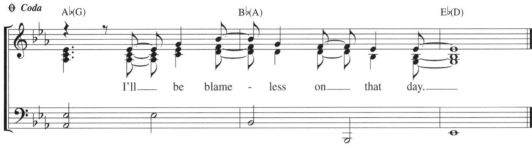

I'll— be blame - less on— that day.—

87a Handle this planet

How shall we handle this planet you loaned us?
Teach us to savour the air and the soil;
show us the plants and the creatures to cherish;
prompt our restraint with the ore and the oil.

Did you not honour the earth by your presence,
tramping the hillside and sailing the lake?
Did you not take life's abundance and share it?
Teach us to value the world for your sake.

If we have damaged the oceans and ice-caps,
if we have torn up the trees out of greed,
or if our science distorts your intentions,
Lord, for both mercy and wisdom we plead!

When you return at the climax of history,
coming to claim what is rightly your own,
may we return to your keeping a planet
fit for a King who is building a throne.

88

The God who set
the stars in space

KINGSFOLD

Words: Timothy Dudley-Smith
Music Arr. David Peacock

Steadily, held back ♩ = 100

1. The God who set the stars in space and gave the planets birth, created for our dwelling place a green and fruitful earth; a world with wealth and

world of order and delight God gave for us to tend, to hold as precious in his sight, to nurture and defend; but yet on ocean,

God, by whose redeeming grace the lost may be restored, who stooped to save our fallen race in Christ, creation's Lord, through him whose cross is

new the wastes of earth again, redeem, restore, repair; with us, your children, still maintain your covenant of care. May we, who move from

God, who set the stars in space and gave the planets birth; look down from heav'n your dwelling place, and heal the wounds of earth; till pain, decay and

211

89

The Lord reigns

Steadily, with a strong beat

Rick Founds
& Todd Collins

1. The Lord reigns, let the earth re-joice.
   hands and wor-ship you, O Lord.

The Lord
(2. I lift my)

Right-eous-ness and truth
For you are the truth Lord

are the foun-da-tions of your throne.
most high a-bove the earth.

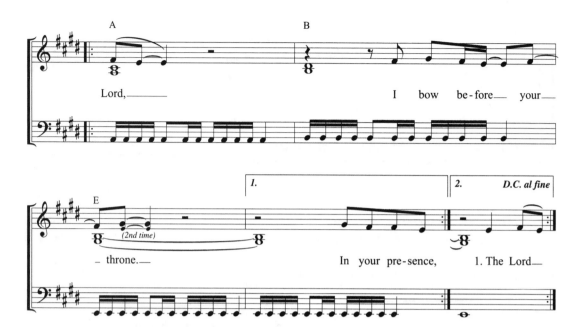

Lord,_____ I bow be-fore__ your__

(2nd time)

1.

2. *D.C. al fine*

__ throne.__ In your pre-sence, 1. The Lord__

89a   Know that I am

When the night comes down
coldly blankly black
and midnight skies
are starless unyielding
like one huge eye staring back
unkindly unblinking
do not despair
know that I am near
I am here.

When the dove stops flying crying
and the songthrush ceases to sing
the peacock loses its feathers
its bright plumage drops and dies
shed you no tear
do not hold your breath in fear
but believe in Me
trust in My powers
to address redress all things
have knowledge of Me
know that I am
I am forever.

Copyright © Fiona Jo Clark

Replacement/chord substitution

Chord substitution means changing the chords of a song to add colour and variety whilst still supporting the original melody and rhythm. This may be as simple as 'pedalling' a single chord over a song that originally had four chords, or it can be more complicated. My encouragement is to get a good chord book then experiment with coloured chords in basic songs.

For example Gmaj can be changed to a Gmaj7 chord
C min chord can be changed to a softer Cmin7
D maj chord can be changed to a D7

The next stage might be to try adding passing chords, for example in the key of G adding Bmin7 between G and C. You would need to adapt the length of each chord to fit the character of the song.

This is just the beginning of your freedom as there are many chords and variants of chords to add such as sharps 5, 9, 11 and flattened 5, augment, min 9th, diminished, plus putting different bass notes under the same chord.

It's vital to ensure that all your band and singers know about any changes. Chord substitution isn't just for keyboard players and guitarists – it can affect anyone who's not playing or singing the melody.

Finally, don't overdo it! Good substitutions can liberate your worship in profound ways, but over-complication can be disastrous. Here's an example of a sequence where all chords are substituted, adding depth and dimension to the arrangement.

'When the music fades' by Matt Redman (in 4/4)
The original song chords (in the key of A) are written above the suggested substitution chords.
When the music fades section:
A | E | Bm7 | E | A | E | Bm7 | Esus4-E
A2 | E/Ab | D/Gb | Abdim | F#m9 | C#m7 | Bm7 | E4-E7

I'll bring you more section:
Bm7-A/C#|E |Bm7-A/C#|Esus4-E |Bm7-A/C#|Esus4|Bm7-A/C#|Esus4-E
Bm7-A |E/Ab|Bm7-A | E/Ab |Bm7-A |E/Ab |Bm7-D2 | E

I leave the chorus to your imagination…

Noel Robinson
www.noelrobinson.com

90

The splendour of the King
(*How great is our God*)

Capo 3 (G)

Chris Tomlin, Jesse Reeves
& Ed Cash

91

The way is open

Graham Kendrick

1. The way is

o - pen, all walls are bro - ken, and we are
o - pen, Je - sus is ri - sen, in high - est
o - pen, let earth be sha - ken, for now in
o - pen, no con - dem - na - tion, now we can

wel - come in the ho - ly place. For - giv'n, ac -
hea - ven as - cend - ed, crowned. God's Son, our
u - nion with Christ we pray. So may his
serve him with con - science cleansed. Work with the

cep - ted, born of the Spi - rit; in Christ we're
bro - ther, our priest for - e - ver, now lives to
long - ings, the Spi - rit's yearn - ings, be on our
Fa - ther, by Spi - rit's pow - er, look - ing to

92

There's a cry in us
(Come Lord come)

Harmony Smith
& Nigel Briggs

Verse

There's a cry in us,_____ an an-cient__ an-them of long - ing__ for your king - dom to come:_____ show__ your glo - ry._____

There's a hope in us,_____ the pro-mise of__ your re - turn - ing:__ King of__ hea - ven__ come in__ your glo - ry.__

Chorus

We join__ with all tribes__ and all na - tions and say:
We join__ with the earth__ that is groan - ing and say:
We join__ with the church__ through the a - ges and say:

'Come,__ Lord, come.'_____ We join__ with the an -

93

There's a dance
(Dance of our God)

Capo 4 (Am)
With a reggae rhythm

Geraldine Latty & busbee

94 There's a song that's rising up inside
(Celebrate)

Ben Cantelon

Positively

1. There's a song that's ri - sing up in - side,
   bat - tle has al - rea - dy been

it's the o - ver - flow of praise.
won, e - ven death you o - ver - came.

Your joy has filled this heart
We crown you King of glo -

a - gain, no, I am not the same.
ry now. You reign vic - tor - ious - ly;

(continued over...)

226

There is an endless song
(How can I keep from singing)

95

Capo 3(D)

Chris Tomlin, Matt Redman
& Ed Cash

Inspired by the Robert Lowry hymn 'How can I keep from singing', c. 1860.

(continued over...)

This song is recorded on the Spring Harvest New Songs 'Shine' album

fall____ down a-gain. I can sing 'cause you pick me up,

sing 'cause you're there, I can sing____ 'cause you hear me, Lord, when I

call to you in pra - yer. I can____ sing with my last breath,

sing____ for I know____ that I'll____ sing with the an - gels____ and the

saints a - round the throne.____ sing.____

D.S. Coda

96

This is the day
(Living free)

Steady rock

Dave Wellington

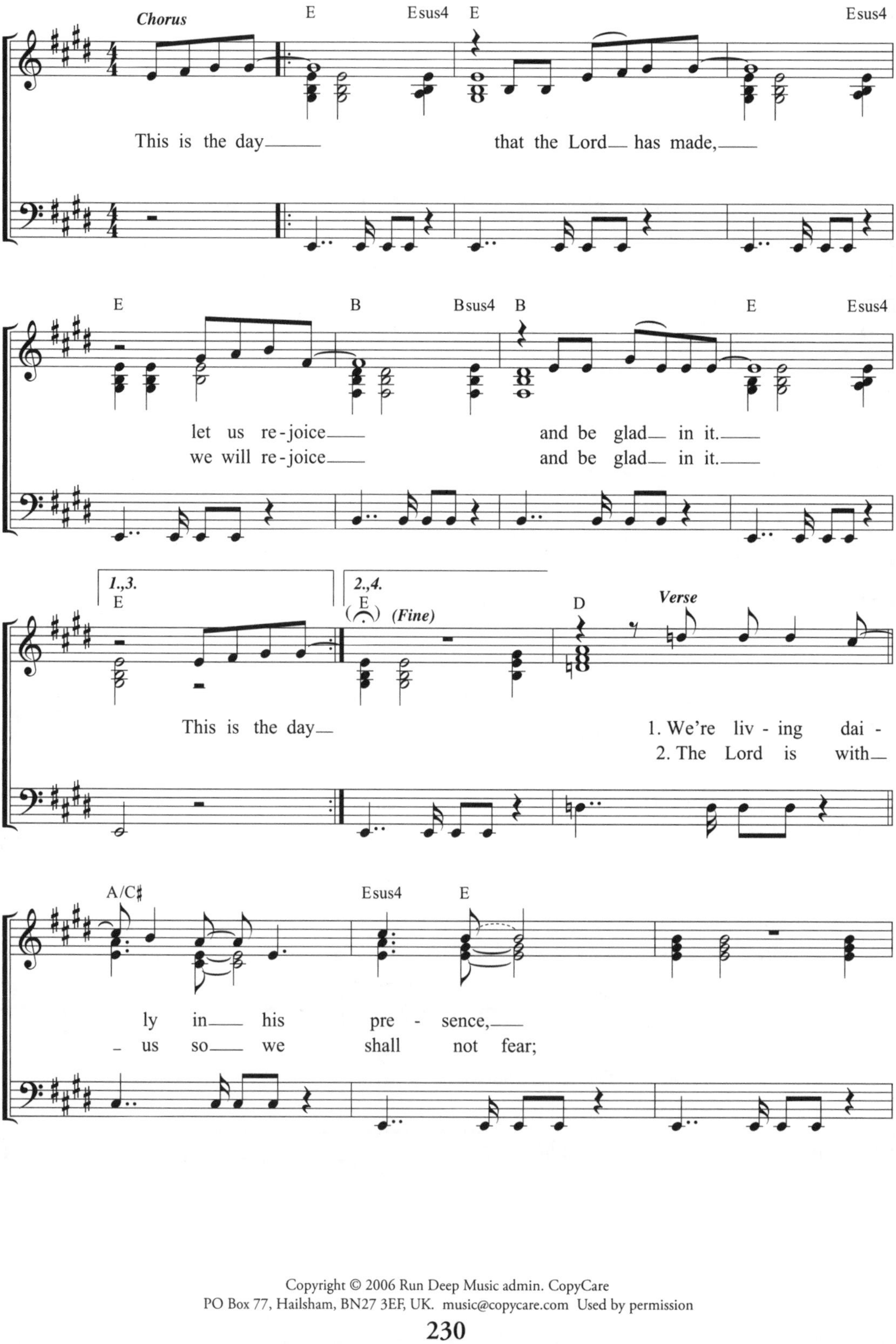

Chorus

This is the day——— that the Lord— has made,———

let us re-joice——— and be glad— in it.———
we will re-joice——— and be glad— in it.———

1.,3.

2.,4. *(Fine)*

Verse

This is the day——

1. We're liv-ing dai-
2. The Lord is with—

ly in— his pre-sence,———
— us so— we shall not fear;

97 Through the love of God our Saviour
(All will be well)

Capo 3(D)

Words: Mary Peters adpt. Leigh Barnard
Music: Leigh Barnard

Moderate 4

1. Through the love of God our Saviour, all will be well;
free and changeless is his favour, all, all is well.
Precious is the blood that healed us, perfect is the grace that sealed

pass through tribulation, all will be well.
Ours is such a full salvation, all, all is well.
Happy still in God confiding; fruitful if in Christ abiding,

pect a bright tomorrow; all will be well.
Faith can sing through days of sorrow, all, all is well.
On our Father's love relying, Jesus ev'ry need supplying,

Chorus

Verse lyrics (underlaid):

- us, strong the hand stretched forth to shield___ us, all must___
ing; stead-fast through the Spi - rit's guid - ing: all must___
ing; or in liv - ing or in dy - ing; all must___

_ be well._____
_ be well._____
_ be well._____ You are ne - ver chang - ing,

con - stant - ly a-maz - ing___ God;___ all will be well.___

Hop - ing in the Sa - viour,

1.,2.

rest - ing in Im-ma-nu - el;___ all will be well.___

(continued over...)

97a   Where Christ walks

Where Christ walks
We will follow

Where Christ stumbles,
We will stop

Where Christ cries
We will listen

Where Christ suffers,
We will hurt

When Christ dies
We will bow our heads in sorrow

When Christ rises again in glory
We will share his endless joy

There is no other way
He is the only way.

98 Through your precious blood

Martyn Layzell

Capo 3 (G)

1. Through your pre - cious blood you have bought peace.
2. Now we have this hope fil - ling our souls,

Dy - ing on a cross, born to set man free.
love so un - de-served, grace now o - ver - flows.

Emp - ty - ing your - self of all ma - je - sty,
So with con - fi - dence, we bold-ly ap - proach,

came in - to this world, a light for all to see.
through the blood you shed, we've ac - cess to your throne.

(continued over...)

This song is recorded on the Spring Harvest Live Worship 'One people' album

99

To the river I am going
(The river)

Capo 3(D)

Gently

Brian Doerksen,
Michael Hansen & Brian Thiessen

1. To the — ri — ver I am go — ing, bring-ing —
wa — ters heal-ing — mer — cy flows with
join — us in the — ri — ver, come, find

sins I can-not bear;— come and cleanse me, come, for-
free — dom from de — spair.— I am go — ing to that —
life be — yond com — pare. He is call — ing, he is

give me; Lord, I — need to meet you there.—
ri — ver; Lord, I — need to meet you there.—
wait — ing; Je — sus — longs to meet you there.—

2. In these — Pre-cious Je — sus, I am

100 To you, O Lord

Moderately

Graham Kendrick

Verse

1. To you, O Lord, I lift up my soul, in you I trust,
2. Show me your ways and teach me your paths, guide me in truth,
3. Re - mem - ber, Lord, your mer - cy and love that e - ver flow

O my God. Do not let me be put to shame,
lead me on; for you're my God, you are my Sa - viour,
from of old. Re - mem - ber not the sins of my youth *D.S.*

3rd verse D.S.

1.,2.

nor let my e - ne - mies tri - umph o - ver me.
my hope is in you each mo - ment of the day.

Chorus

No - one whose hope is in you will e - ver be put to shame;

that's why my eyes are on you, O Lord. Sur - round me, de - fend me,

This song is recorded on the Spring Harvest iScape 'No one like you' album

101

Turn my face again
(Turn my face)

Capo 5(C)

Martin Layzell

1. Turn my face again towards the cross
2. Kneel me down again before the cross
3. Lead me to the place your body lay,

on the mount of Calvary.
where they pierced your hands and feet.
where the stone lies rolled away.

Take me back again to ponder on the life
King so humble in a crown of thorns. The scars
Clothed in majesty and victory, you rose

you gave, the price you paid to save me.
you wear were mine to bear for ever.
again and death is slain for ever.

1st time only

102

We have heard the call
(As Jesus walked)

Gently

Martyn Layzell

Verse

1. We have heard the call to go in-to the world with seed to sow. With liv-ing words with-in our hearts, we will walk as Je-sus walked.

2. Live a life of sa-cri-fice, and die to our hu-man de-sires. To see the poor and not pass by, is to walk as Je-sus walked, help us walk

3. Be good news in all we do, bind up the bro-ken heart-ed, heal the sick and raise the dead, is to walk as Je-sus walked, help us walk

246

103

We wait in hope for you
(Unfailing love)

Nigel Briggs, Rich Bull
Matt Loose & Phil Squires

Seriously

Verse

We wait in hope for you, our shel - ter and our truth.

You are al - ways faith - ful to your word.

Con - sume our hearts and minds, and be the au - thor of this life.

Your king - dom come, your will be done.

In these times of doubt and sor - row, peo - ple need a

(continued over...)

This song is recorded on the Spring Harvest New Songs 'Wonderful Saviour' album

hope to cling— to. Your love is an an-chor in— the storms— of life, for-

Chorus

e - ver faith - ful.— Un - fai - ling love,——— you

Last time to Coda

ne - ver let— us down.— Your pro-mise is— a - live.—

D.C.

We pro - mise is— a - live.—

Mid section

When col - oured dreams——— fade— to grey,—— un -

248

fail - ing love.___ When the night___ crowds out the day,___ un -

fail - ing love.___ When there's no words left___ to say,_____

God's love re - mains.

D.S. al Coda

Coda

104 When I call on your name
(Love came down)

Capo 3(G)

Ben Cantelon

105 When there's sorrow in my heart
(Psalm 13)

Words: Nigel Briggs
Music: Trent

With feeling, strong in the chorus

This song is recorded on the Spring Harvest New Songs 'Wonderful Saviour' album

How long, how long for your mer-cy— and your

king-dom— to come?— How long, how— long— to—

wait? 1. When there's to wait?

I still re-

joice in your sal-va-tion and trust in— your un-fail-ing love.—

(continued over...)

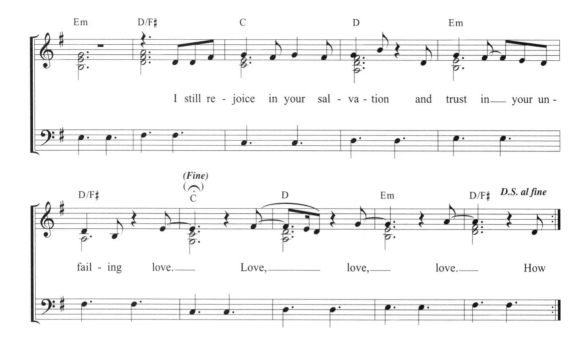

I still re-joice in your sal-va-tion and trust in your un-fail-ing love. Love, love, love. How

---

105a   A joy-filled proclamation

Let us shout for joy to our Creator God
He is the one who set the earth in motion
He is the one who watches over us
He is the one who upholds our world.
Be strong, take heart, all we who hope in the Lord.

Let us rejoice in our Sustainer God
He is the one who nourishes us
He is the one who supplies our need
He is the one who renews us day by day
Be strong, take heart, all we who hope in the Lord.

Let us give praise to our Redeemer God,
He is the one who forgives us
He is the one who gives us peace and reconciliation
He is the one who mends the broken
Be strong, take heart, all we who hope in the Lord.

106

When trouble strikes
and fear takes root
(A woman's care)

DIED FOR LOVE

Words: John L. Bell
& Graham Maule

Gently

1. When trou - ble strikes and fear____ takes root and
2. Our wan - d'ring minds be - lieve the worst and
3. God says, 'See how a wo - man cares; can
4. 'My dear - est daugh - ter, fond - est son, my
5. Then praise the Lord through faith____ and fear, in

dreams are dry____ and sense un - sound; when hope be - comes____ a
ask, as faith and fer - vour fade, 'Has God now turned____ his
she for - get____ the child she bore? Ev'n if she did,____ I
wea - ry folk in ev - 'ry land, your souls are cra - dled
ho - ly and____ in help - less place; for height and depth____ and

bar - ren waste,____ then doubts____ like moun - tains soar____ a - round.
back on us,____ for - sak - ing those____ he loved____ and made?'
shan't for - get:____ though feel - ing lost,____ I love____ you more.'
in my heart,____ your names____ are writ - ten on____ my hand.'
heav'n and hell____ can't keep____ our lives____ from God's em - brace.

107

When trials come

Capo 3(C)

Keith & Kristyn Getty

Moderately ♩ = 88

Bb(G) Eb(C) Ab6(F) Eb/Bb (C) Eb(C)

1. When— tri - als come, no lon - ger fear, for— in the pain our
   in the night, I know your peace; the— breath of God brings
   turn to wis - dom not my own, for— ev - 'ry bat - tle
   I am wea - ry with the cost, I— see the tri - umph
   day all things will be made new; I'll— see the hope you

Ab(F) Bb(G) Eb/G (C) Ab(F) Eb/G (C) N.C. Cm7(Am)

God draws near, to— fire a faith worth more— than— gold;
strength to me. And— new each morn - ing mer - cy— flows,
you have known. My— con - fi - dence will rest— in— you;
of the cross; so— in its sha - dow I— shall— run,
called me to. And— in your king - dom paved— with— gold

Eb/G (C) Abmaj7(F) Bb(G) Cm7(Am) Eb/G (C)

— and— there his faith - ful - ness is— told, and— there his
— as trea - sures of the dark - ness— grow, as— trea - sures
— your love en - dures, your ways are good, your love en -
— till He com - pletes the work be - gun, till he com -
— I'll— praise your faith - ful - ness of— old, I'll— praise your

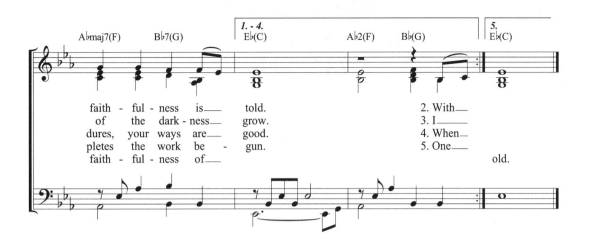

faith - ful - ness is___ told.
of the dark - ness___ grow.
dures, your ways are___ good.
pletes the work be - gun.
faith - ful - ness of___

2. With___
3. I___
4. When___
5. One___

old.

107a   Your hand of mercy

Your hand of mercy is on me
for evermore.
Your hand of mercy will guide me;
my path is sure.
Hands that strained upon a tree,
Saviour's hands that reach for me;
compassion pour.
No love greater than my friend –
will I ever understand?
Scars upon your hand.

Your heart of mercy is for me
for evermore.
Your heart of mercy has called me;
I am secure.
King of glory, King of love,
blessings falling from above;
I gaze in awe.
No love greater than my friend –
will I ever understand?
Lord, your sacrifice was planned.
Scars upon your hand.

108

Where do I go
when I'm feeling down?
(My help)

Mark Beswick
& Howard Francis

Capo 3 (D)

Where do I go_____ when I'm__ feel-ing down,_____ who do I call__
- fer my foot__ to be moved,_____ the one__ who keeps__

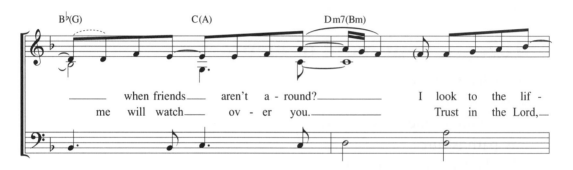

_____ when friends__ aren't a-round?_____ _____ I look to the lif-
me will watch__ ov-er you._____ _____ Trust in the Lord,__

ter of__ my_____ head, Je-sus, my Sa-viour, Lord__ and friend.
_ bel-ieve,__ have faith,_____ lift up your voice__ to him__ and say:

He will not suf- ___ I will lift up mine eyes__ to the hills_____ from

whence com - eth my strength,_____ my help com - eth from the

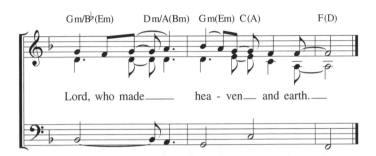

Lord, who made_____ hea - ven___ and earth.___

108a   The name of the Lord our God
From Psalm 20: 7

Some trust in chariots, some trust in horses;
We trust the name of the Lord our God.
Some trust in politics, some trust in riches;
We trust the name of the Lord our God.
Some trust technology, some trust their heroes;
We trust the name of the Lord our God.

Some place their hope in their own wit or wisdom:
Our hope is God, the Eternal One.
Some place their hope in a friend or a lover:
Our hope is God, the Eternal One.
Some place their hope in their work or their leisure:
Our hope is God, the Eternal One.

Some look for guidance in stars or in omens:
Christ is our Saviour, our Lord, our Hope.
Some pin their dreams to a lottery ticket:
Christ is our Saviour, our Lord, our Hope.
Some have no thoughts of a brighter tomorrow:
Christ is our Saviour, our Lord, our Hope.

Some trust in chariots, some trust in horses;
Christ is our Saviour, our Lord, our Hope.

109

Who can know?
(I stand in awe)

Martyn Layzell

With quiet intensity

1. Who can know the mind of our Cre-a-tor,
2. Who has weighed the dust of ev-'ry moun-tain,
3. You have seen the end from the be-gin-ning,

who can speak of won-ders yet un-seen;
who has walked the my-st'ries of the deep;
you have been be-fore the world be-gan;

who can reach the height of un-der-stand-ing, to
who has laid the earth on its foun-da-tion, and
you have reached to me with-in my dark-ness, and

1. play the notes of wis-dom's me-lo-dy?

110
Who could imagine
(A greater song)

Paul Baloche
& Matt Redman

1. Who could imagine a melody true enough to tell of your mercy? Who could imagine a harmony sweet enough to tell of your love? I see the heavens proclaiming you day after day, and I know in my heart that there must be a way to sing a greater song, a great-

2. Who could imagine a symphony grand enough to tell of your glory? Our highest praise but a feeble breath, a whisper of your thunderous worth.

This song is recorded on the Spring Harvest New Songs 'Wonderful Saviour' album

(continued over...)

Hal - le - lu - jah, we wan-na lift you high - er. Hal - le - lu - jah,

we wan-na lift you high - er. we wan-na lift you high - er.

Hal - le - lu - jah, we wan-na lift you high - er. Hal - le - lu - jah,

we wan-na lift you high - er.

Song writing for congregations – Part 2

Continued from page 119

Rich in scripture

Every Sunday we face a congregation of people whose lives may look perfect but who desperately need words of truth to penetrate every part of their lives – intellectually, emotionally, spiritually. Lets make sure as writers or as leaders that every song is feeding our people. The apostle Paul addresses public worship in Colossians 3;16 to "let the word of Christ dwell in us richly, as we sing Psalms, hymns and spiritual songs".

Learn from the past

As a modern hymn writer I've always found that in folk music, old hymns, classic ballads and classical music there is a limitless resource – when we look at the great melodists of old we are privileged to stand on tall shoulders and learn from them. In the contemporary genre I think we have to listen to what arena audiences sing the loudest – although it does tend to limit them to short term usage as what was popular ten years ago almost never is now.

Hard work

I've never had a very high success rate as a melody writer – in comparison to the number of melodies I've written – the importance of working at it an any other craft cannot be overstated – also often a melody eventually makes it after many drafts.

It finishes with the congregation

Each week as we review 'songs' whether that is songs we write or songs we select or lead for congregational worship the final analysis cannot be based on musical arrangement, or vocal performance, nor even the many aspects surrounding the congregational singing it boils down to – were these words feeding our congregation and was the congregation engaged in passionate singing.

Keith Getty
www.gettymusic.com

111

Who is my mother?

HELEN

Words: Shirley Erena Murray
Music: Jane Marshall

1. Who is my mo-ther, who is my bro-ther? All those who
2. Dif-f'rent-ly a-bled, dif-f'rent-ly la-belled, wi-den the
3. Love will re-late us— co-lour or sta-tus can't se-gre-
4. Bound by one vi-sion, met for one mis-sion, we claim each

gath-er 'round Je-sus Christ: Spi-rit-blown peo-ple, born from the
cir-cle 'round Je-sus Christ: crut-ches and stig-mas, cul-ture's e-
gate us, 'round Je-sus Christ: fa-mi-ly fail-ings, hu-man de-
o-ther 'round Je-sus Christ: here is my mo-ther, here is my

gos-pel, sit at the ta-ble 'round Je-sus Christ.
nig-mas, all come to-ge-ther 'round Je-sus Christ.
rail-ings— all are ac-cep-ted 'round Je-sus Christ.
bro-ther, kin-dred in Spi-rit, through Je-sus Christ.

112

Why do you wait?
(Jesus is waiting)

Steady 4

Noel Robinson & Sam Blake

Why do you wait? Re - ceive him to-day;___ he is wait-ing to

an-swer your call.___ He can heal your bro-ken heart___ to-day,___ so___

come, oh come, oh___ come. ___ come. Je-sus is wait-ing, Je-sus is

wait - ing, Je-sus is wait-ing to an-swer your call.___ Je-sus is

wait - ing to an-swer your call.___

113 Worthy, you are worthy

Matt Redman

With a 'half time' feel

114

You chose the cross
(Lost in wonder)

Capo 3(G)

Steadily

Martyn Layzell

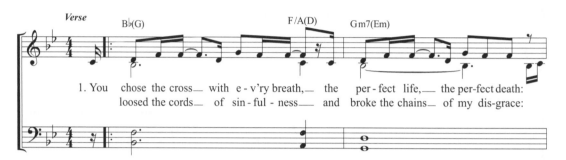

Verse

Bb(G)   F/A(D)   Gm7(Em)

1. You chose the cross— with e-v'ry breath,— the per-fect life,— the per-fect death:
loosed the cords— of sin-ful-ness— and broke the chains— of my dis-grace:

Eb(C)   Bb(G) F/A(D)   Bb(G)   F/A(D)

you chose— the cross.— A crown of thorns— you wore for us,— and
you chose— the cross.— Up from the grave— vic-to-ri-ous— you

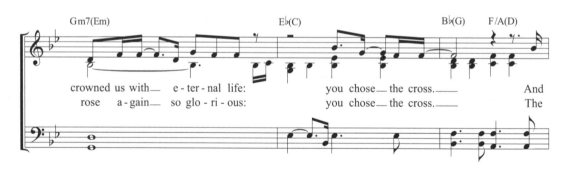

Gm7(Em)   Eb(C)   Bb(G) F/A(D)

crowned us with— e-ter-nal life: you chose— the cross.— And
rose a-gain— so glo-ri-ous: you chose— the cross.— The

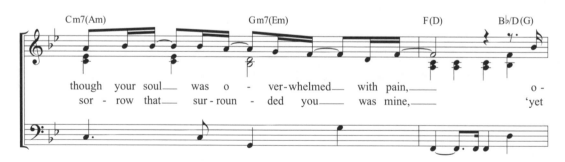

Cm7(Am)   Gm7(Em)   F(D)   Bb/D(G)

though your soul— was o-ver-whelmed— with pain,— o-
sor-row that— sur-roun-ded you— was mine, 'yet

This song is recorded on the Spring Harvest 'He is risen' Easter classics album

be - di - ent___ to death___ you o - ver - came.   I'm lost in
not my will___ but yours___ be done'___ you   said.

won - der,___ I'm lost in___ love,   I'm lost in praise for - e - ver more.___

_____ Be-cause of Je - sus'___ un-fail - ing___ love,   I am for -

gi - ven,___ I am re-stored.___   (2. You)

115 You give rest
(I will say)

Nathan & Lou Fellingham
& busbee

Capo 2(G)
Steady pace

1. You give rest to the wea - ry, you bring strength to the weak;
2. You can come in the si - lence. You can come in the noise.

as they wait in your pre - sence,
Bring-ing peace in a mo - ment,

there is grace for their need. So I'll wait, I'll wait, yes, I'll wait;
bring-ing com-fort and joy.

I'll wait for you. I will say of the Lord, 'he is my

This song is recorded on the Spring Harvest New Songs 'Shine' album and on the Spring Harvest Live Worship 'One people' album

Copyright © 2005 Thankyou Music/The Livingstone Collective/Adm. by worshiptogether.com songs
excl. UK & Europe, Adm. by kingswaysongs.com tym@kingsway.co.uk Used by permission

116 You stood before creation
(The stand)

You who speak
(You are)

Precision Centre

♩ = 94

Verse

You who speak and it's done,—— de-clar-ing

that which is yet to come. Ex-ist-ing by—— your sov-'reign might;

the path to truth,—— the path to life. E-ter-ni-

ty is in the palm of your hands,—— yet you dwell in the hearts of men.—

(continued over...)

118

Your voice
(Lord, you are here)

Calvin Hollingworth

Gently

1. Your voice is call - ing us, your love is draw - ing us, your touch is heal - ing us; your Spi - rit lead - ing us to you.
2. Your hands are shap - ing us, your grace is grow - ing us, your mer - cy hold - ing us; your Spi - rit lead - ing us to you.
3. Your wind is shak - ing us, your rain re - fresh - ing us, your peace is still - ing us; our weak - ness glo - ri - ous in you.

And we place our feet on ho-

119

You're praiseworthy
(Praiseworthy)

Capo 3 (G)
With joy

Nick Herbert
& Matt Redman

This song is recorded on the Spring Harvest Live Worship 'One people' album

Coda

Hal - le - lu - jah, hal - le - lu - jah, you're praise -
wor - thy, so praise - wor - thy.

119a Bathing and washing

Accepting your free gift once and for all
we bathed to take away our human stain,
but now from daily work we come to you
our tired and dusty feet to wash again.

Always we live beneath your sheltering blood,
as once they did on that Passover night,
yet constantly we need its cleansing power,
reviving spirits weakened in the fight.

You laid aside your outer garments then,
taking the apron of a roman slave,
then went to give away your very life
that we redemption's priceless gift might have.

And as we see the measure of your love,
stooping to make your servantship complete,
we ask that we, forgetting rank and power
in genuine care may wash each other's feet.

120 You've closed your ears to the sound of our songs
(You listen out)

Steadily

Andy Flannagan

let it e - cho all a - round; may it be a sweet, sweet

_ sound, may it be a sweet, sweet sound.

Last time D.S. al Fine

(Fine)

Mid section

Speak up for those whose voi - ces will get lost,

speak up for those left car-ry-ing our cross, (a-gain.)

car-ry - ing our cross.

D.C. (v.1)

Guitar Chords

Introduction

A good chord vocabulary is essential for a guitarist to feel confident when playing in worship, especially when the situation may involve reading a previously unseen piece of music or picking up a song quickly by ear. The chords on these pages are arranged in 'families' according to key. This is a beneficial way of remembering chords as most songs stick to these groupings. For each key, the first row shows the simplest form of each chord and the second line gives a more interesting substitution. The third line shows the chords most commonly used by guitarists derived by keeping some sort of pedal tone ringing in each chord and the fourth line shows inverted chords with an alternate bass note.

Also included are the Roman Numerals and Nashville Numbers associated with each chord. If you've not come across these before, they are simply an easy way of numbering each chord within a key. This is useful as it means you can take any chord progression in one key and instantly transpose it to another. Furthermore you can try out any of the chords in each column that corresponds to the relevant Roman Numeral and see if there is chord type or inversion which still fits but adds a different flavour. Experimentation like this may open up creative chord progressions that serve as a catalyst to help you to worship in fresh ways or to write new songs.

Please see the CD-ROM section of Spring Harvest Distinctive Sounds – More than a Song album and the Academy of Music Ministry's website at www.nexustrust.co.uk for details of more material relating to developing these skills.

	Roman	I	II	III	IV	V	VI	VII
	Nashville	1	2	3	4	5	6	7
Key of C	3-note chord (triad)	C	Dm	Em	F	G	Am	Bdim
	4-note chord	C maj7	D m7	E m7	F maj7	G7	A m7	Bm7♭5
	Alternative substitute	C	D7sus4	Em7	F sus2	G5	A m7	Dsus4/B
	Alternative bass note	C/E	Dm/F	Em/G	F/A	F/G	Am/E	

For all chords in the key of C# or Db, use the chords from the key of C with capo 1

Guitar Chords

	Roman	I	II	III	IV	V	VI	VII
	Nashville	1	2	3	4	5	6	7
Key of D	3-note chord (triad)	D	Em	F#m	G	A	Bm	C#dim
	4-note chord	D maj7	Em7	F#m7	G maj7	A7	Bm7	C#m7♭5
	Alternative substitute	D sus2	Em9	F#m7	G6sus2	A7sus4	Bm11	A add9/C#
	Alternative bass note	D/F#	Em/B	F#m/A	G/B	G/A	Bm/F#	

For all chords in the key of D# or E♭, use the chords from the key of D with capo 1

	Roman	I	II	III	IV	V	VI	VII
Key of E	3-note chord (triad)	E	F#m	G#m	A	B	C#m	D#dim
	4-note chord	E maj7	F#m7	G#m7	A maj7	B7	C#m7	D#m7♭5
	Alternative substitute	E5	F#m11	G#madd♭6	A add9	B add4	C#m7	D#alt
	Alternative bass note	E/G#	F#m/C#	G#m/D#	A/C#	A/B	C#m/G#	

For all chords in the key of F, use the chords from the key of E with capo 1

For all chords in the key of F# or Gb, use the chords from the key of E with capo 2

287

Guitar Chords

Roman	I	II	III	IV	V	VI	VII
Nashville	1	2	3	4	5	6	7

Key of G

	I	II	III	IV	V	VI	VII
3-note chord (triad)	G	Am	Bm	C	D	Em	F#dim
4-note chord	Gmaj7	Am7	Bm7	Cmaj7	D7	Em7	F#m7♭5
Alternative substitute	G	A7sus4	Dsus4/B	Cadd9	Dsus4	Em7	G/F#
Alternative bass note	G/D	Am/C	Bm/D	C/G	C/D	Em/G	

For all chords in the key of G# or A♭, use the chords from the key of G with capo 1

Key of A

	I	II	III	IV	V	VI	VII
3-note chord (Triad)	A	Bm	C#m	D	E	F#m	G#dim
4-note chord	Amaj7	Bm7	C#m7	Dmaj7	E7	F#m7	G#m7♭5
Alternative substitute	Asus2	Bsus4	C#m7	D6sus2	Eadd9	F#m11	Eadd9/G#
Alternative bass note	A/E	Bm/F#	C#m/E	D/A	D/E	F#m/A	

For all chords in the key of A# or Bb, use the chords from the key of A with capo 1

For all chords in the key of B, use the chords from the key of A with capo 2

Richard Stephenson & Andy Flannagan

288

Scripture Index

Scripture Index cont'd

Scripture Index cont'd

Spoken Worship Index

Based on Genesis 2:15,19-20, Psalm 8:6-8, 24:1; John 1:14, ... John 6:11, 1 John 1:1, Matthew 5:1,14:19, Mark 4:35-36, 6:41, Luke 9:16, Revelation 15:15

Thematic Index

Thematic Index cont'd